THE
ADDRESS BOOK
HOW TO REACH ANYONE WHO is ANYONE

Michael Levine

A Perigee Book

Perigee Books
are published by
The Putnam Publishing Group
200 Madison Avenue
New York, NY 10016

Library of Congress Cataloging-in-Publication Data

Levine, Michael.
   The address book.
   Rev. ed. of: The new address book. ©1986.
   "A Perigee book."
   1. United States—Social registers. 2. United
States—Directories. 3. Celebrities—Directories.
4. Associations, institutions, etc.—United States—
Directories. 5. Associations, institutions, etc.—
Directories. I. Levine, Michael. Address book.
II. Title.
E154.5.L48 1988   973'.025   88-5860
ISBN 0-399-51487-2

Printed in the United States of America
1   2   3   4   5   6   7   8   9   10

A Donation and Dedication to the Spirit of Samantha

Noting the tremendous success of the first edition of *The Address Book: How to Reach Anyone Who is Anyone*, I have made a donation to the Samantha Smith Foundation, and am dedicating this edition of the book to Samantha Smith. The Samantha Smith Foundation is a nonprofit organization founded by Jane Smith in memory of her daughter and in honor of her daughter's historic peace and goodwill trip to the Soviet Union in 1985.

Samantha's trip to Russia proves the power of a letter and a dream. I couldn't think of a better way to honor her memory.

Samantha Smith gained worldwide attention in 1985 when she innocently sent a letter to then General Secretary Yuri Andropov. To the surprise of Samantha and the world, Andropov both answered her letter and invited the child to visit the Soviet Union in hopes of furthering world peace.

When she accepted my donation, Jane Smith said, "Mr. Levine's book encourages people to go for their dreams, write people of influence, and perhaps change the world a little. I plan to use the book myself."

Donations to the Samantha Smith Foundation may be sent to: Samantha Smith Foundation, 9 Union Street, Hallowell, ME, 04347.

Acknowledgments

*Friendship is the only cement that
will hold the world together.*

My heartfelt thanks to the following dear people in my life:

My literary agent, Bart Andrews.

My friends at Putnam Publishing, Gene Brissie, Marilyn Ducksworth, Phyllis Grann, Suzanne Herz, Eleanor Holdridge, Judy Linden, Janis Vallely, and Neal Sigman.

My family, Arthur, Marilyn, and Patty Levine.

My brilliant associate, Mitchell Schneider.

My office family, Kim Akhtar, Michelle Bega, Lori DeAngelis, Cary Goldberg, Elizabeth Hotsko, Lisa Kahre, Scott Loane, Monique Moss, Jason McCloskey, Marcee Rondan, Caren Roth, Sandy Tabuchi, Jeff Wagner, David Wayne, Leah West, and Julie Wheeler.

My special friends, Nancy Behrman, Rana Bendixen, Ken Bostic, Bill Calkins, Karen L'Heureux, Nancy Mager, John McKillop, Dennis Prager, Richard Imprescia, Lori Kleinman, Harry Sandler, Jerry Swartz, Josh Trabulus, Erline White, Allen Esses.

My head of research, John Aubrey Taylor.

But, most of all, my appreciation to everyone who has used *The Address Book* over the years, and who has had the courage to write to people they don't personally know in an effort to make their dreams come true.

Dear Friend:

I was barely three months old when I first stepped on stage. Actually, I was carried on by my parents, but it was me who got the applause as Baby New Year in 1921. I don't remember it, of course, but they say I took a bow and asked for top billing the next day. I settled for my own dressing room. All kidding aside, after all these years, it's still the applause which makes me want to take the stage or do a movie or television. Making that connection with an audience is magical. It's the greatest feeling in the whole world.

That's why I wanted to write the foreword to this latest edition of Michael Levine's *The Address Book*. As a performer, I know that it's not only applause that makes the good times better and pulls you through the bad times, but also the fan letters. Experts tell me that when a television station or newspaper receives a letter they estimate that the writer actually represents the feelings of 100 or more people who didn't get motivated enough to write themselves. Well, I'll tell you this, letters to the people in this book mean a bundle more than that.

Someone once said that fans are people who let an actor know he's not alone in the way he feels abut himself. It's not modest but it's true. After years in vaudeville and silent movies, then talkies, television, and the stage, I've had more ups and downs than wives. That's a lot. A career like mine can make you mighty insecure. Receiving one special letter on a day at exactly the right time can change your whole mood for the better. It's the fans, their heart and generosity, that made me go on. Someone else once said that the public is never wrong. I'll second that, too.

You may not believe we actually read the letters that come in. We sure do. And so do the television networks and movie studios and so on. Believe me, people pay attention to what you think, what you like or don't like, who you want to see more of and who less. With a personal letter you become more than two hands clapping in a dark auditorium, you become a voice, a name, a person who took the time and effort to write us. It's appreciated, even when you have criticism. At least then we know someone out there is listening and watching. It tells us that you care.

Writing letters may be the only way you have to make your voice heard. But where do you address a letter to your favorite celebrity? That's where *The Address Book* comes in. It can keep you in touch with people you may never get a chance to meet face-to-face. Now this is really reaching out and touching someone. It's sure a lot better than driving by stars' homes in Beverly Hills in a tour bus and waving at the gardener.

You want to say something to someone? Write them. You've discovered something to applaud? Write them. You want to complain? Don't get mad, write them. That's what's so wonderful about what you have in your hands right now. It's a powerful tool (the saying that the pen in mightier than the sword is so true) and yet it's personal too. It can make a real connection between you, wherever you are, and that person on the television or the movie screen or behind the desk of a big corporation. Without it, all you can do is talk back to the screen or throw your shoe at the TV. Back in vaudeville, they'd throw vegetables. That can get expensive, not to mention messy. Postage stamps are cheaper, cleaner too. *The Address Book* is your passport to go anywhere, speak to anyone (hero or villain), and all for the price of a postage stamp.

Thousands of folks are listed here. There are celebrities, corporate executives, politicians, athletes, musicians, scientists, artists, dozens of organizations and charities, and lots more. They're all here: from AAMCO Transmissions to Xerox, from Yassir Arafat to Dr. Seuss, from Michael Jackson to Madonna, from Bruce Springsteen to Princess Diana. Anyone who's anyone, says Michael Levine. Even I'm included!

I like that. You can write me anytime you want. I couldn't have lasted as long as I have in show business without fans. No one can. I've been blessed. Without those fans out there, Mickey Rooney would not have been possible. I've enjoyed a great career and I'm grateful. You see, it's fans who make *our* dreams come true. And perhaps by writing to people in this book, some dreams of your own can happen. Even if it's just knowing that your favorite star might soon be reading what you have to say.

Come to think of it, there are a few people I'd like to write myself and tell them what I think, give them a piece of my mind. So, if you'll excuse me, it's time to put pen to another sheet of paper. But it's been real good talking to you. Now go on and write someone. They're waiting to hear from you. Hopefully, they'll be hearing applause.

God Bless.

Mickey Rooney
P.O. Box 5028
Thousand Oaks, CA
91360

Introduction

The biggest question regarding writing to notables is, "How can I make sure the notable receives my letter?" Well, the number-one reason mail to notables is left unanswered is that it is addressed improperly and never reaches its intended destination. A letter addressed simply to "Barbra Streisand, Hollywood, California" will find its way only to the dead-letter file of the post office. And so, here's this book: complete, accurate addresses that will get your mail to the homes, offices, agents, studios, or managers of the addressees.

The following are other commonly asked questions:

Q. Will the notable personally read my letter?

A. I have been unable to find even one notable, no matter how busy or important—ranging right up to the president of the United States—who doesn't personally read some of his mail. That doesn't mean notables read and answer every single piece, but it should offer encouragement to people who write to them. Amazing things have been accomplished with letters as long as they have the proper mailing address.

Q. Are there any professional tricks you can reveal that might improve the chances of having my letter read and answered?

A. Yes! Here are several important things to remember:

1. Always include a self-addressed envelope. This is the single most important bit of advice I can offer to people writing to notables. Because of the unusually high volume of mail they receive, *anything* you can do to make it easier for them to respond is going to work in your favor.
2. Keep your letters short and to the point. Notables are usually extremely busy people, and long letters tend to be set aside for "future" consideration. For instance, if you want an autographed picture of your favorite TV personality, don't write three pages of prose to explain your request.
3. Make your letter as easy to read as possible. This means type it or, at the very least, handwrite it *very neatly*. Avoid crayons,

markers, and even pencils. And don't forget to leave some margins on the paper.

4. Be sure to include your name and address (even on all materials that you include with your letter, in the event the materials are separated from your letter). You would be amazed how many people write letters without return addresses and then wonder why they never hear from the person to whom they wrote!

Q. What are the don'ts in writing to notables?

A. Actually, there are very few don'ts but here are some good general rules to follow:

1. Don't send food to notables. Due to spoilage and security matters, it cannot be eaten anyway. (Would *you* eat a box of homemade brownies given to you by a total stranger?)
2. Don't send—or ask for—money.
3. Don't wrap gifts in large boxes with yards of paper, string, and tape around them. In other words, not everyone is fortunate enough to have a crowbar on hand. And—again—don't forget to include your name and address on all material you send.

Q. Do corporation heads pay attention to mail from a single individual?

A. Wow, do they! Most corporation heads rose to their lofty positions because they were better problem-solvers than their company peers. Good corporation heads are zealous about finding solutions to written complaints (especially if you have sent copies of your complaint letters to appropriate consumer organizations). A recent survey of corporations showed that 88 percent of all letters of complaint were resolved. Therefore, the old adage, "When you have a problem, go to the top," appears to be accurate. Likewise, corporation executives greatly appreciate hearing good news (satisfaction, extra service, helpful employees, and so forth). For a sample complaint letter and additional tips, see page 10.

Q. What about politicians? Are they really interested in what I have to say?

A. You better believe it. Politicians have a standard rule of thumb: For every letter they receive, they estimate that one hundred people who didn't take the time to write are thinking the same thought as the letter expresses. So you can calculate the effect of your single letter by multiplying it by one hundred!

Q. Do celebrities consider mail important?

A. Second only to money! All notables—especially entertainment fig-ures—keep a very close watch on their mail. It is a real indication of what people are thinking and feeling. Often the notable is surrounded by a small group of close associates who tend to isolate the star from the public. Your letter helps break down this barrier.

Q. Why have you included infamous people in your book?

A. Where is it written that mail should only be filled with praise and congratulations? I thought people would enjoy shaking their fist at their favorite villain. So, go get 'em!

Q. What do most people say in their letters?

A. Usually people are very kind and sincere, writing what they would say or ask if they had the opportunity to do so in person. This is especially true of children, who are *extremely* honest. On the other hand, infamous people and others who are out of favor with the public predictably receive hostile and angry letters.

Q. What if my letter is returned to me?

A. Most of the people listed in *The Address Book* are movers and shakers, and, thus, highly transient, changing their addresses far more often than the average person. Their mail is usually forwarded to them, but occa-sionally a letter may be returned to the sender. If this should happen to your letter, first check to make sure that you have copied the address correctly. If you wish to locate another address for the person to whom you are writing, begin your search by writing to him or her in care of the company or assocation with which they have been most recently associated. For example, if a musician or singer has last recorded an album with a specific record company, write in care of that company; a sports figure might be contacted through the last team he or she was associated with; an author through his or her most recent publisher; and so forth.

Tips for Writing an Effective Complaint Letter

1. Include your name, address, and home and work phone numbers.
2. Type your letter, if possible. If it is handwirtten, be sure it is neat and legible.
3. Make it brief and to the point. Include all pertinent facts (date of transaction, item involved, store, and so forth) and what you believe would be a fair and just settlement of the problem. Attach documentation to support your case; send copies, not originals.
4. Remember, the person reading your letter is not personally responsible for your problem, but may be responsible for solving it. Therefore, avoid writing a sarcastic, threatening, or angry letter. It may lessen your chances of getting the complaint resolved.
5. Send copies of your letter to a lawyer, the Better Business Bureau, Chamber of Commerce, consumer advocates, and so forth. This technique carries a lot of weight and shows that you mean business.
6. Keep copies of your letter and all related documents and information.

Sample Complaint Letter

Your Address
City, State, Zip Code
Date

Appropriate Person
Company Name
Street Address
City, State, Zip Code

Dear (*Appropriate Name*):

Specific background information__   On (*date*), I purchased a (*name of product with serial or model number*). Upon taking it home and

State problem clearly and concisely _____

following the enclosed instructions for its use, I discovered that your product does not perform satisfactorily. Specifically, it does not *(describe function)* as I expected it would based on the advertising and packaging.

Ask for satisfaction _____

Enclose copies, not originals ____

State time parameter _____

Include phone numbers _____

I would appreciate your *(state the action you want)*. Enclosed you will find copies of my records *(receipt, warranty, guarantee, canceled check, etc.)* to verify the purchase. I look forward to your reply within *(reasonable period of time)* before seeking third-party assistance. You may contact me at the above address or by phone at *(home and office numbers)*.

Thank you for your prompt resolution of this problem.

Sincerely,

Your name

Send copies of letter to all appropriate persons and organizations __

cc: Chamber of Commerce
 Related Associations
 Dealer Through Whom
  Product Was Purchased
 Local Media or Consumer
  Advocate

Dealing with the U.S. Post Office

Stopping "Junk" Mail

What's become commonly referred to as "junk" mail really drives some people nuts, so The Direct Mail Marketing Association, Inc., offers a free service allowing consumers to have their names added to or deleted from national advertising lists.

Copies of a booklet, *How Did They Get My Name?* which explains consumer mailing lists, are available without charge from DMMA, 6 E. 43rd St., New York, NY 10017.

The Mail Order Merchandise Rule

The mail order rule adopted by the Federal Trade Commission in October 1985 provides that, when you order by mail, you must receive the merchandise when the seller says you will. If you are not promised delivery within a certain time period, the seller must ship the merchandise to you no later than thirty days after your order comes in. If you don't receive it shortly after that thirty-day period, you can cancel your order and get your money back.

How the Rule Works

The seller must notify you if the promised delivery date (or the thirty-day limit) cannot be met. The seller must also state what the new shipping date will be and give you the option to cancel the order and receive a full refund or agree to the new shipping date. The seller must also offer you a free way to send back your answer, such as a stamped envelope or a postage-paid postcard. *If you don't answer, it means that you agree to the shipping delay.*

The seller must provide notification if the shipping delay is going to be more than thirty days. You then can agree to the delay or, if you do not agree, the seller must return your money by the end of the first thirty days of the delay.

If you cancel a prepaid order, the seller must mail you the refund within seven business days. Where there is a credit sale, the seller must adjust your account within one billing cycle.

It would be impossible, however, for one rule to apply uniformly to such a varied field as mail order merchandising. For example, the rule does not apply to mail order photo finishing, magazine subscriptions, and other serial deliveries (except for the initial shipment); to mail order seeds and growing plants; to COD orders; or to credit orders where the buyer's acocunt is not charged before shipment of the merchandise.

How to Complain About a Postal Problem

When you have a problem with your mail service, complete a Consumer Service Card, which is available from letter carriers and at post offices. This will help your postmaster respond to your problem. If you wish to telephone a complaint, a postal employee will fill out the card for you.

The Consumer Advocate represents consumers at the top management level in the Postal Service. If your postal problems cannot be solved by your local post office, write to the Consumer Advocate. His staff stands ready to serve you. Write to: The Consumer Advocate, U.S. Postal Service, Washington, D.C. 20260-6320. Or phone: 1-202-245-4514.

Pornography

You can stop the mailing of unsolicited sexually oriented advertisements to you by filling out Form 2201, *Application for Listing Pursuant to 39 USC 3010*, at your local post office. Thirty days after your name has been added to the Postal Service reference listing, any mailer who sends you sexually oriented advertisements is subject to legal action by the United States Government.

You may also stop the mailing of further advertisements to you that you consider "erotically arousing or sexually provocative." Fill out Form 2150, *Notice for Prohibitory Order Against Sender of Pandering Advertisement in the Mail*, at your post office for this purpose.

Common Questions

Q. What should I do if I suspect that a letter I mailed has been lost?
A. Fill out Postal Form 1510, *Mail Loss/ Rifling Report*, which is available at any post office. That way you'll have a record that shows your letter was mailed but not delivered. And your report could help postal inspectors trace the lost mail.

Q. What's the best way to prevent parcel loss or damage?

A. Pack your object in a strong container that will protect it. Cushion the contents of your parcel to make sure it doesn't move inside the box. Don't tie your package with string; use reinforced tape to close the package and seal flaps. Don't use wrapping paper—it could tear off during shipment. Make sure the address is written clearly on the package.

Q. How long should it take for a first-class letter to travel across the nation?

A. It should take three days.

Q. What's the difference between certified mail and registered mail? And what is return receipt service?

A. Certified mail is used mainly to provide proof that an important document or other item has been mailed. You should use certified mail to send important papers dealing with taxes, real estate, insurance, or investments.

Registered mail is the safest type of mail for valuables. It requires signatures of postal workers at every step along the way, from mailing to delivery. This service is designed for irreplaceable documents such as stock certificates and other valuables.

Return receipt service provides you with a receipt verifying that the letter or package you sent was actually delivered. You can request a receipt for any registered or certified mail, express mail, COD letters or packages, or any item insured for more than twenty-five dollars.

How to Use This Book

Most of the entries in this book are names of persons notable in some field. You also will find many companies, agencies, and institutions. These are listed under the name of the organization. This is done so that you can find the address of IBM, for example, without knowing the name of its president. The entry will then give you the address and the president's name.

Are You Anyone?

   The Address Book is updated regularly and you can play an active role in this procedure. If you are a notable in any field, or know someone who is, send the name, mailing address, and some documentation of the notability (newspaper clippings are effective) for possible inclusion in our next edition.

   Also, we are very interested in learning of any success stories that may have resulted from *The Address Book*.

   If you have found *The Address Book: How to Reach Anyone Who is Anyone* to be useful, you may also find its sequel, *The Corporate Address Book: How to Reach the 1,000 Most Important Companies in America* (Perigee), of assistance. In *The Corporate Address Book*, we reveal, in an easy-to-use format, the direct addresses and phone numbers of the thousand most important companies in America that affect each of our lives.

   Thank you.

Michael Levine, Author
The Address Book
8730 Sunset Blvd., Sixth Floor
Los Angeles, CA 90069

Write to Me

During the last few years, I have received tens of thousands of letters, ranging from loving to vituperative, from owners of *The Address Book* and *The New Address Book*. Despite the overwhelming task of answering this mail, I rather enjoy the letters. In fact, some have downright warmed my heart when the world was feeling especially cold.

But, please, a couple of rules if you write:

- Remember to include a self-addressed, stamped envelope. For reasons of both time and expense, this is the only way that I can respond to mail; so, unfortunately I've had to draw the line—no SASE, no reply.
- I need your comments. While I confess that I'm partial to success stories, comments from purchasers of the book have helped me a great deal for future editions; so fire away. As Colonel Oliver North said, "The good, the bad, the ugly."
- Many people have written to request addresses of people not listed in the book. As much as I would like to, I simply can't open up this can of worms. Requests for additional addresses are carefully noted and considered for inclusion in future editions.
- Receiving a photo from someone who writes adds an entirely new dimension to the letter, so feel free. That's right, enclose a photo of yourself. After all, from the photo on the back cover, you know what I look like, and I'm rather anxious to see you.

Keep those cards and letters coming.

Michael Levine
8730 Sunset Blvd., Sixth Floor
Los Angeles, CA 90069

Aach, Herbert
404 E. 14th St.
New York, NY 10009
Painter

AAMCO Transmissions, Inc.
One Presidential Blvd.
Bala-Cynwyd, PA 19004
Robert Morgan,
chairman of the board

A & A Poultry Farms, Inc.
106-10 N. Lincoln St.
West Unity, OH 43570
Jay H. Wattles, Jr., president

Aaron, Betsy
c/o ABC News
7 W. 66th St.
New York, NY 10023
Journalist

Aaron, Henry
P.O. Box 4064
Atlanta, GA 30302
Baseball player, holds record for
career home runs (755)

Aaronson, Stuart
NCI Bldg. 37
Bethesda, MD 20814
Cancer researcher

Abba
Box 26072 S-100 41
Stockholm, Sweden
Pop music group

Abbado, Claudio
c/o Columbia Artists Management, Inc.
165 W. 57th St.
New York, NY 10019
Conductor

Abbott, George
1270 Ave. of the Americas
New York, NY 10020
Playwright, producer

Abbott, Philip
c/o Nelson Co.
5400 Shirley Ave.
Tarzana, CA 91356
Actor

Abbott Laboratories, Inc.
Abbott Park Rt. 137
North Chicago, IL 60064
Robert A. Schoellhorn,
chairman of the board and CEO

ABC
c/o Ron Weisner,
NuVision Entertainment
9200 Sunset Blvd., Penthouse 15
Los Angeles, CA 90069
Pop group

**Abdul-Jabbar, Kareem
(Lew Alcindor)**
P.O. Box 10
Los Angeles, CA 90012
Basketball player

Abelson, Philip Hauge
1515 Massachusetts Ave. NW.
Washington, DC 20005
Physical chemist, institutional exec.

Aberstain, Jose Manuel
c/o S. Methodist Church
Dance Division
Dallas, TX 75275
Ballet master

Abraham, F. Murray
888 7th Ave., Number 1800
New York, NY 10106
Actor

Abrams, Talbert
124 N. Larch St.
Lansing, MI 48933
*Aviator, explorer, photogramme-
trist*

Acapulco Restaurants
2690 E. Foothill Blvd.
Pasadena, CA 91107
Martin Brody, CEO

**Accorsi, William Ernest,
Jr.**
11001 Bonita Ave.
Owings Mills, MD 21117
*Personal manager to football play-
ers*

AC-DC
1888 Century Park E., Suite 1400
Los Angeles, CA 90067
Heavy metal rock group

Ace Hardware Corp.
2200 Kensington Ct.
Hinsdale, IL 60521
*Theodore Costoff,
chairman of the board*

Ackerman, Bettye Louise
c/o Sue Golding Agency
6380 Wilshire Blvd.
Los Angeles, CA 90048
Actress

A. C. Nielsen
Nielsen Plaza
Northbrook, IL 60062
N. Eugene Harden, president

Ad-A-Girl Personnel, Inc.
8525 SW. 92nd St.
Miami, FL 33156
Dee Speigel, president and CEO

Adams, Brooke
c/o Phil Gersh Agency, Inc.
222 N. Canon Dr.
Beverly Hills, CA 90210
Actress

Adams, Bryan
c/o Bruce Allen Talent
406 68 Water St.
Vancouver, BC. Canada
V6B 1A4
Rock singer, songwriter

Adams, Joey
355 Lexington Ave., Suite 200
New York, NY 10017-6603
Comedian

Adams, John Franklin
2970 Rockingham Dr. NW.
Atlanta, GA 30327
Economist, educator

Adams, Richard George
26 Church St.
Whitchurch, Hampshire, England
Author

Adato, Perry Miller
c/o WNET 13
356 W. 58th St.
New York, NY 10019
Documentary producer and writer

Adler, Richard
8 E. 83rd St.
New York, NY 10028
Composer, lyricist

Adriani, John
Charity Hospital
New Orleans, LA 70140
Physician, Emeritus educator

Advanced Micro Devices, Inc.
901 Thompson Pl.
Sunnyvale, CA 94086
*W. J. Sanders III,
chairman of the board and CEO*

Aetna Life & Casualty Co.
151 Farmington Ave.
Hartford, CT 06156
William O. Bailey, president

Afghan Freedom Fighters Fund
P.O. Box 693
Boulder, CO 80306

Agrigenetics Corp.
3375 Mitchell Ln.
Boulder, CO 80301
*Robert W. Scher,
chairman of the board*

A-Ha
151 El Camino Dr.
Beverly Hills, CA 90212
Pop music group

Ahenakew, David Frederick
Assembly of First Nations
222 Queen St
Ottawa, ON. Canada
K1P 5V9
National Indian chief

Aikins, Claude
151 El Camino Dr.
Beverly Hills, CA 90212
Actor

Ainge, Danny
c/o Boston Celtics, Boston Garden
North Station
Boston, MA 02114
Basketball player

Airborne Freight Corp.
3101 Western Ave.
Seattle, WA 98121
Robert S. Cline,
chairman of the board and CEO

Air Host, Inc.
474 S. Perkins Extn.
Memphis, TN 38117
William R. Smith, president

Air Supply
Siegal & Feldstein
1990 Bundy Dr.
Number 590
Los Angeles, CA 90025
Pop music group

Alabama
c/o Dale Morris & Associates
818 19th Ave. S.
Nashville, TN 37203
Country-rock group

Al-Anon
P.O. Box 862
Midtown Station
New York, NY 10018-0862
Attn: Carol Kuney, public information

Alaska Airlines, Inc.
19300 Pacific Highway S.
Seattle, WA 98188
Bruce Kennedy, president and CEO

Al-Assad, Hafez
Presidential Palace
Damascus, Syria
President of Syrian Arab Republic

Prince Albert
Palais De Monaco
Boite Postal 518
98015 Monte Carlo, Monaco
Son of Princess Grace

Albert, Eddie (Edward Albert Heimberger)
2121 Ave. of the Stars
Suite 410
Los Angeles, CA 90067
Actor

Albert, Marv
c/o NBC Sports, Room 720F
30 Rockefeller Plaza
New York, NY 10112
Sportscaster,
television station director

Albertsons, Inc.
250 Parkcenter Blvd.
Boise, ID 83706
Warren E. McClain,
chairman of the board and CEO

Alcoholics Anonymous
P.O. Box 459
Grand Central Station
New York, NY 10017
John Bragg, general manager

Alcott, Amy Strum
1250 Shoreline Dr., Suite 200
Sugar Land, TX 77478
Golfer

Alda, Alan
c/o Martin Bregman Productions,
Inc.
641 Lexington Ave.
New York, NY 10022
Actor, writer, director

Aldredge, Theoni
240 E. 27th St., Suite 12G
New York, NY 10016
Costume designer

**Aldrin, Edwin Eugene, Jr.
(Buzz)**
11652 Chenault St., Number 106
Los Angeles, CA 90049
*Former astronaut,
science consultant*

Alexander, Jane
c/o William Morris Agency
1350 Ave. of the Americas
New York, NY 10019
Actress

Alexander, Lamar
Office of the Governor

State Capitol
Nashville, TN 37219
Governor of Tennessee

Alfonsin, Raul R.
Casa Rosada
Buenos Aires, Argentina
President of Argentina

**Ali, Muhammad
(Cassius Marcellus Clay)**
P.O. Box 187
Berrien Springs, MI 49103-0187
*Former world heavyweight box-
ing champion, businessman*

Allain, William A.
P.O. Box 139
Jackson, MS 39205
Governor of Mississippi

Allen, Betty
645 St. Nicholas Ave.
New York, NY 10030
Mezzo-soprano

Allen, Irwin
c/o Columbia Pictures
Burbank, CA 91505
*Motion picture writer, director,
producer*

Allen, Karen
c/o Press Relations,
Paramount Pictures
One Gulf & Western Plaza
New York, NY 10023
Actress

Allen, Nancy
1888 Century Park E., Suite 1400
Los Angeles, CA 90067
Actress

Allen, Phillip
222 N. Canon Dr.
Beverly Hills, CA 90210
Actor

Allen, Stephen Valentine Patrick William (Steve)
15201 Burbank Blvd.
Van Nuys, CA 91411
Television humorist, songwriter

Alley, Kristie
10390 Santa Monica Blvd.
Suite 310
Los Angeles, CA 90025
Actress

Allied Van Lines, Inc.
25th Ave. and Roosevelt Rd.
Maywood, IL 60153
Dennis I. Mudd, CEO

Allison, Robert
140 Church St.
Hueytown, AL 35023
Stock car driver

Allman, Gregg
P.O. Box 4331
Marietta, GA 30061
Singer, songwriter, keyboardist

Allstate Insurance Co.
Allstate Plaza
Northbrook, IL 60062
Donald F. Craib, Jr.,
chairman of the board and CEO

Alpert, Herb
1416 N. La Brea Ave.
Hollywood, CA 90028
Musician,
cofounder of A & M Records

Alpha Beta Stores Co.
777 Harbor Blvd.
La Habra, CA 90631
Donald H. Kohler, president

Altman, Robert B.
c/o Sandcastle Productions
128 Central Park S., Suite 4B
New York, NY 10019
Motion picture writer, producer,
and director

Alzado, Lyle
151 El Camino Dr.
Beverly Hills, CA 90212
Football player

The Amanda Foundation
2178 Roscomare Rd.
Los Angeles, CA 90077
Animal protection organization
Attn: Gillian Lange

America West Airlines
222 S. Mill Ave.
Tempe, AZ 85281
Edward R. Beauvais,
chairman of the board and CEO

American Airlines, Inc.
Dallas/Fort Worth Airport
Dallas, TX 75261-9616
Robert L. Crandall,
president and CEO

American Banana Co., Inc.
Pier Number 2, Harlem River
Bronx, NY 10451
Alfred Allega, president

American Broadcasting Companies, Inc.
1330 Ave. of the Americas
New York, NY 10019
John B. Sias, president and CEO

American Express Co.
American Express Plaza
New York, NY 10004
James D. Robinson III,
chairman of the board and CEO

American Lifelobby (Right to Life)
P.O. Box 490
Stafford, VA 22554
Randy Scott

American Motors Corp.
27777 Franklin Rd.
Southfield, MI 48034
Paul Tippett, chairman of the
board

American Political Items Collectors
P.O. Box 340339
San Antonio, TX 78234

Joseph D. Hayes, secretary.
Organization studies and pre-
serves materials from U.S. political
campaigns

American Sports Collectibles
P.O. Box 475
Horsham, PA 19044
"Buck" Lane, president. Company
sells authentic autographs and
other sports memorabilia

American Stock Exchange, Inc.
86 Trinity Pl.
New York, NY 10006
Arthur Levitt, Jr.,
chairman of the board and CEO

American Telephone & Telegraph Co.
550 Madison Ave.
New York, NY 10022
C. L. Brown, chairman of the
board

Amoco Corp.
200 E. Randolph Dr.
Chicago, IL 60601
Richard M. Morrow, CEO

Amway Corp.
7575 E. Fulton Rd.
Ada, MI 49301
Richard De Vos, president. Manu-
factures and distributes cleaning
products

Anderson, Ivan Delos
1060 Flamingo Rd.
Laguna Beach, CA 92651
Impressionist painter

Anderson, Jack
1401 16th St. NW.
Washington, DC 20036
Syndicated political columnist

Anderson, Laurie
c/o Liz Rosenberg
3 E. 54th St.
New York, NY 10022
Performance artist, songwriter

Anderson, Loni
3955 Alomar Dr.
Sherman Oaks, CA 91423
Actress

**Anderson, Lynn
(Rene Anderson)**
c/o International Creative
Management
40 W. 57th St.
New York, NY 10019
Singer

Anderson, Mellisa Sue
9200 Sunset Blvd., Suite 1009
Los Angeles, CA 90069
Actress

Anderson, Paul
c/o Scott Meredith Literary
Agency
845 3rd Ave.
New York, NY 10022
Science fiction writer

Andress, Ursula
8185 Gould Ave.
Los Angeles, CA 90046
Actress

Andretti, Mario
53 Victory Ln.
Nazareth, PA 18064
Race car driver

HRH The Prince Andrew
Buckingham Palace
London SW1 England
The duke of York

Andrews, Julie
1888 Century Park E., Suite 1616
Los Angeles, CA 90067
Actress, singer

Andrews, Patti
P.O. Box 1793
Encino, CA 91316
Singer

Anger, Kenneth
American Federation of Arts,
Film Program
41 E. 65th St.
New York, NY 10021
Filmmaker, author

Anheuser-Busch Companies, Inc.
One Busch Pl.
St. Louis, MO 63118-1852
August A. Busch III, president

Anka, Paul
Box 100
Carmel, CA 93921
Singer, composer

HRH The Princess Anne
Gatcombe Park
Gloucestershire, England
Daughter of Queen Elizabeth II

Annenberg, Walter
P.O. Box 98
Rancho Mirage, CA 92270
Founder TV Guide magazine, former U.S. ambassador to England

Ann-Margret (Ann-Margret Olsson)
1888 Century Park E., Suite 1400
Los Angeles, CA 90067
Actress, performer

Another World Viewer Alliance
71 Berry St.
Pittsburgh, PA 15205
Sue Leonard, president

Ant, Adam
45/53 Sinclair Rd.
London W14 England
Pop music singer, songwriter

Anti-Defamation League of B'nai B'rith
823 United Nations Plaza
New York, NY 10017
Kenneth Bialkin, chairman

Anton, Susan
15190 Ventura Blvd., Suite 1602
Encino, CA 91403
Actress

Antonioni, Michelangelo
Via Vincenzo Tiberio 18
Rome, Italy
Motion picture director

Apple Computer, Inc.
20525 Mariani Ave.
Cupertino, CA 95014
John Scully, president and CEO

Appollonia
9000 Sunset Blvd., Suite 1112
Los Angeles, CA 90069
Actress, singer

Aquino, Corazon
Malacanang Palace
Manila
Philippines
President of the Philippines

Arafat, Yassir
Palais Essasada La Marsa
Tunis, Tunisia
Palestine Liberation Organization leader

Aragalli, Giacomo
c/o Robert Lombardo Association
61 W. 62nd St.
New York, NY 10023
Opera singer

Archer, Dan
270 E. Blithedale Ave.
Mill Valley, CA 94941
Retired football player, architect

Archerd, Army
c/o Variety
1400 N. Cahuenga Blvd.
Hollywood, CA 90028
Entertainment columnist

Arensdorf, Mike
3074 Gibraltar Ave.
Costa Mesa, CA 92626
*President, M.A. Scale Models,
company that builds small scale
models, specializing in race car
kits*

Arkin, Alan
8899 Beverly Blvd.
Los Angeles, CA 90048
Actor

Arkoff, Samuel Z.
9200 Sunset Blvd., PH3
Los Angeles, CA 90069
*Motion picture executive, pro-
ducer*

Arledge, Roone
c/o ABC-TV
1330 Ave. of the Americas
New York, NY 10019
*Group president, ABC News and
Sports*

Armani, Giorgio
c/o Giorgio Armani Fashion Corp.
650 5th Ave.
New York, NY 10019
Fashion designer

Armatrading, Joan
1416 N. La Brea Ave.
Hollywood, CA 90028
Singer, songwriter

Armstrong, Bess
8267 Hollywood Blvd.
Los Angeles, CA 90069
Actress

Armstrong, Neil
31 N. Broadway
Lebanon, OH 45036
First man to walk on the moon

Arnaz, Lucie Desiree
249 W. 45th St.
New York, NY 10036
Actress

Arness, James
P.O. Box 49004
Los Angeles, CA 90049
Actor

Arnold, Danny
9200 Sunset Blvd., Suite 920
Los Angeles, CA 90069
*Television writer, producer,
and director*

Arnold, Eddy
Box 97
Brentwood, TN 37027
Singer

Arquette, Rosanna
1888 Century Park E., Suite 1400
Los Angeles, CA 90067
Actress

Arthur, Beatrice
151 El Camino Dr.
Beverly Hills, CA 90212
Actress

Arum, Robert
919 3rd Ave.
New York, NY 10022
Sports events promoter

Asencio, Diego
U.S. Embassy, Brazil
APO Miami, 34030
U.S. ambassador to Brazil

Ash, Mary Kay Wagner
8787 Stemmons Freeway
Dallas, TX 75247
Chairman, Mary Kay Cosmetics, Inc.

Ashby, Hal
7950 Sunset Blvd.
Hollywood, CA 90046
Motion picture director

Ashe, Arthur
c/o Pro Serve

888 17th St.
NW. Washington, DC 20006
Tennis player

Ashford, Nicholas
1350 Ave. of the Americas
New York, NY 10019
Singer, songwriter

Ashland Oil, Inc.
1000 Ashland Dr.
Russell, KY 41169
John R. Hall,
chairman of the board and CEO

Ashley, Elizabeth
151 El Camino Dr.
Beverly Hills, CA 90212
Actress

Asimov, Isaac
10 W. 66th St.
Apt. 33A
New York, NY 10023
Author of 328 science fiction and nonfiction books

Askin, Leon
9401 Wilshire Blvd., Suite 1000
Beverly Hills, CA 90213
Director, actor, producer, and writer

Asleep at the Wheel
6060 N. Central Expressway,
Number 428
Dallas, TX 75202
Country music group

THE ADDRESS BOOK

Asner, Edward
3955 Lankershim Blvd.
North Hollywood, CA 91604
Actor

Associated Milk Producers
6609 Blanco Rd.
San Antonio, TX 78284
Irwin Elkin, president

**Association for Retarded
Citizens of the U.S.**
2501 Avenue J
Arlington, TX 76006
V. K. "Warren" Tashjian, president

**Association on Third
World Affairs, Inc.**
1740 R. St. NW.
Washington, DC 20009
Dr. Lorna Hahn

**Astin, Patty Duke
(Anna Marie Duke)**
9100 Sunset Blvd., Suite 300
Los Angeles, CA 90069
Actress

Atari Games Corp.
675 Sycamore
Milpitas, CA 95035
Nakajima Hideyuki, president

Atkins, Christopher
8966 Sunset Blvd.
Los Angeles, CA 90069

**Atlantic Richfield Co.
(ARCO)**
515 S. Flower St.
Los Angeles, CA 90051
*Robert O. Anderson,
chairman of the board*

Atlantic Starr
c/o Cole Classic Management
7080 Hollywood Blvd., Suite 603
Hollywood, CA 90028
Pop music group

**Atomic Bowling Lanes,
Inc.**
E. 27 Augusta
Spokane, WA 99207
Dr. Curran D. Higgins, president

**Attenborough, Sir Richard
(Samuel Attenborough)**
Old Friars
Richmond Greene
Surrey, England
Motion picture producer, director

Auberjonois, Rene Murat
124 W. 79th St.
New York, NY 10024
Actor

Auchincloss, Louis Stanton
67 Wall St.
New York, NY 10005
Author

**Auerbach, Arnold Jacob
(Red Auerbach)**
c/o Boston Celtics, North Station
Boston, MA 02114
*Basketball exec.,
chosen all-time NBA coach by the
National Coaches Association*

Austin, Tracy
c/o International Management
Group
One Erieview Plaza
Cleveland, OH 44114
Tennis player

Autry, Orvon Gene
Box 710
Los Angeles, CA 90078
*Singer, actor, broadcasting and
baseball team exec.*

Avaloone, Michael Angelo
80 Hilltop Blvd.
East Brunswick, NJ 08816
Author

Avelrod, Todd M.
3601 W. Sahara Ave.
Las Vegas, NV 89102
*President, American Museum of
Historical Documents*

Avian, Bob
890 Broadway
New York, NY 10003
*Tony award winning choreogra-
pher*

Avildsen, John
45 E. 89th St.
New York, NY 10128
Motion picture director

Avon Products, Inc.
9 W. 57th St., 31st Floor
New York, NY 10019
*Hicks B. Waldron,
chairman of the board and CEO*

Axton, Hoyt
P.O. Box 1077
Hendersonville, TN 37075
Singer, composer

Aykroyd, Dan
9200 Sunset Blvd., Suite 428
Los Angeles, CA 90069
Actor, writer, comedian

Ayres, Lew
151 El Camino Dr.
Beverly Hills, CA 90212
Actor

Azenberg, Emanuel
165 W. 46th St.
New York, NY 10036
Theatrical producer

Babbitt, Bruce
Office of the Governor
1700 W. Washington St.
Phoenix, AZ 85007
Politician

Babilonia, Tai
8730 Sunset Blvd.
6th Floor
Los Angeles, CA 90069
Olympic figure skater

**Bacall, Lauren
(Betty Joan Perske)**
c/o STE Representation Ltd.
1776 Broadway
New York, NY 10019
Actress

Bach, Barbara
Tittenhurst Park
Ascot, Surrey, England
Actress

Bach, Catherine
1400 Davana Terrace
Sherman Oaks, CA 91423
Actress

Bacharach, Burt
910 N. Crescent Dr.
Beverly Hills, CA 90210
Pianist, composer

Bach-Y-Rita, Paul
600 Highland Ave.
Madison, WI 57305
*Neurophysiologist,
rehabilitation medicine specialist*

Badham, John
7950 Sunset Blvd.
Hollywood, CA 90046
Motion picture director

Baez, Joan
P.O. Box 1026
Menlo Park, CA 94026
Folksinger, activist

Bailey, F. Lee
109 State St.
Boston, MA 02109
Attorney

Bailey, Pearl
Box L
Lake Havasu City, AZ 86403
Singer, actress

Bain, Conrad Stafford
1901 Ave. of the Stars
Los Angeles, CA 90067
Actor

Baines, Harold
c/o Chicago White Sox
Comiskey Park
Dan Ryan at 35th St.
Chicago, IL 60616
Baseball player

Baio, Scott
5555 Melrose Ave.
Los Angeles, CA 90038
Actor

**Baird, Bill
(William Britton Baird)**
40 5th Ave.
New York, NY 10011
Puppeteer, author

Baker, Anita
c/o BNB & Associates
804 N. Crescent Dr.
Beverly Hills, CA 90210
Soul singer

Baker, Howard Henry, Jr.
White House
1600 Pennsylvania Ave.
Washington, DC 20501
*Chief of staff for Reagan
administration, lawyer, former
senator*

Baker, James Addison III
Office of the Secretary,
Dept. of Treasury
15th and Pennsylvania Ave.
NW. Washington, DC 20220
Secretary, Department of Treasury

Baker, Joe Don
1000 Santa Monica Blvd.
Suite 305
Los Angeles, CA 90067
Actor

Baker, Lenox Dial
Duke Hospital
Box 3706
Durham, NC 27710
Orthopedist, genealogist

Baker, Ronald Lee
Indiana State University
Terra Haute, IN 47809
Folklore educator

Bakshi, Ralph
Gang, Tyre & Brown, Inc.
6400 Sunset Blvd.
Los Angeles, CA 90028
Motion picture producer and director

**Baldwin Piano & Organ
Co.**
1801 Gilbert Ave.
Cincinnati, OH 45202
Harold Smith, president

Balin, Marty
10 Waterville St.
San Francisco, CA 94124
*Musician, cofounder of the
Jefferson Airplane and the KBC
Band*

THE ADDRESS BOOK

Ball, Lucille
1000 N. Roxbury Dr.
Beverly Hills, CA 90210
Actress, comedienne

Ball, Robert M.
236 Massachusetts Ave., Suite 405
NE. Washington, DC 20002
*Social security, welfare, and health
policy specialist*

Ballet Lingerie, Inc.
135 Madison Ave.
New York, NY 10016
Joe Polonecki, president

Bally Manufacturing Corp.
8700 W. Bryn Mawr Ave.
Chicago, IL 60631
*Robert E. Mullane,
chairman of the board and president*

Balsinger, David Wayne
P.O. Box 10428
Costa Mesa, CA 92627
*Author, publisher, advertising
exec.*

Balukas, Jean
c/o Billiard Congress
14 S. Linn St.
Iowa City, IA 52240
Pro pocket billiard player

Bananarama
9200 Sunset Blvd., Penthouse 15
Los Angeles, CA 90069
Pop music group

Bancroft, Ann
P.O. Box 900
Beverly Hills, CA 90213
Actress

Bandy, Moe
1609 Hawkins St.
Nashville, TN 37203
Country music recording artist

The Bangles
8335 Sunset Blvd., 3rd Floor
W. Hollywood, CA 90069
Pop music group

Bank of America
555 California St.
San Francisco, CA 94104
*Leland S. Prussia,
chairman of the board*

Bankers Trust Co.
P.O. Box 318
Church St. Station
New York, NY 10015
*Alfred Brittain III,
chairman of the board and CEO*

Banks, Jeffrey
1384 Broadway
New York, NY 10018
Fashion designer

Banner, Bob
8687 Melrose Ave., Suite M-20
Los Angeles, CA 90069
Television director

Barbara, Agatha
The Palace
Valetta, Malta
President of the Republic of Malta

Barbeau, Adrienne
P.O. Box 1334
North Hollywood, CA 91604
Actress

Barbee, Victor
c/o American Ballet Theatre
890 Broadway
New York, NY 10003
Ballet dancer

Barbera, Joseph
3400 W. Cahuenga Blvd.
Hollywood, CA 90068
*Cartoonist, cofounder of
Hanna-Barbera Productions*

**Bare, Bobby
(Robert Joseph Bare)**
59 Music Square W.
Nashville, TN 37203
*Country music singer and song-
writer*

**Barker, Bob
(William Robert Barker)**
c/o Goodson-Toddman
Productions
6430 Sunset Blvd.
Hollywood, CA 90028
Television personality

Barkin, Ellen
8899 Beverly Blvd.
Los Angeles, CA 90048
Actress

Barnard, Dr. Christiaan
Waiohal, South Cross Dr.
Constantia, Cape Town
South Africa
Scientist

Barnes, Martin McRae
Department of Entomology
UC Riverside
Riverside, CA 92521
Entomologist

Barnett, Arthur Doak
c/o Johns Hopkins School for
Advanced International Studies
1740 Massachusetts Ave.
NW. Washington, DC 20036
Political scientist

Barnouw, Erik
39 Claremont Ave.
New York, NY 10027
*Author,
specialist in broadcast history*

Baron, Samuel
321 Melbourne Rd.
Great Neck, NY 11021
Flutist

Barrett, Rona
P.O. Box 1410
Beverly Hills, CA 90213
Entertainment columnist

Barrie, Barbara
151 El Camino Dr.
Beverly Hills, CA 90212
Actress

Barry, Gene
151 El Camino Dr.
Beverly Hills, CA 90212
Actor

Barry, Marion Shepilou, Jr.
Office of the Mayor
District Bldg., 14th and E Sts.
Washington, DC 20004
Mayor of Washington

Barrymore, Drew
Box 1305
Woodland Hills, CA 91364
Actress

Barsalona, Frank
3 E. 54th St.
New York, NY 10022
Rock group agent

Bartlett, Boyd C.
c/o Deere & Co.
John Deere Rd.
Moline, IL 61265
President and CEO, Deere & Co.

Bartlett, Hal
9200 Sunset Blvd., Suite 908
Los Angeles, CA 90069
*Motion picture producer and
director*

Bartlett, Tommy
P.O. Box 65
Wisconsin Dells, WI 53965
Impresario

Barty, Billy John
10954 Moorpark St.
North Hollywood, CA 91602
Actor

Baryshnikov, Mikhail
c/o American Ballet Theatre
890 Broadway
New York, NY 10003
*Ballet dancer, actor,
ballet company exec.*

BASF Corp.
8 Campus Dr.
Parsippany, NJ 07054
*Dr. Jurgen F. Strube,
president and CEO*

Basinger, Kim
8436 W. 3rd St., Suite 650
Los Angeles, CA 90048
Actress

**Basket People Home
Parties Ltd.**
599 Norwich Ave.
Taftville, CT 06380
*David L. Phipps, president.
Makers of some of America's
finest baskets*

Baskin-Robbins Ice Cream Co.
31 Baskin-Robbins Rd.
Glendale, CA 91201
Robert Hudecek,
chairman of the board

Bass, Saul
7039 W. Sunset Blvd.
Los Angeles, CA 90028
Graphic designer, filmmaker

Bassett, Charles Andrew Lockerman
630 W. 168th St.
New York, NY 10032
Pioneer in using pulsing electromagnetic fields to treat diseases and disorders in humans and animals

Bateman, Jason
P.O. Box 333
Woodland Hills, CA 91365
Actor

Bateman, Justine
P.O. Box 333
Woodland Hills, CA 91365
Actress

Batiuk, Thomas
1703 Kaiser Ave.
Irvine, CA 92714
Cartoonist,
creator of "Funky Winkerbean"

Battlestein, Sandra L.
3506 Tartan Ln.
Houston, TX 77025
Author

Bauer, Martin
9255 Sunset Blvd., Suite 710
Los Angeles, CA 90069
Theatrical producer

Bauman, Jon
c/o Shankman DeBlasio, Inc.
185 Pier Ave.
Santa Monica, CA 90405
Entertainer

Baumgarten, Craig
3970 Overland Ave.
Culver City, CA 90232
President, Lorimar Motion Pictures

Bausch & Lomb
One Lincoln First Tower
Rochester, NY 14604
Daniel E. Gill, president and CEO

Baxter-Birney, Meredith
9255 Sunset Blvd., Suite 1105
Los Angeles, CA 90069
Actress

Bazell, Robert
c/o NBC News
30 Rockefeller Plaza
New York, NY 10112
NBC News science correspondent

The Beach Boys
101 Mesa Ln.
Santa Barbara, CA 93109
Rock band

Beacher, Lawrence Lester
Whittingham Place
West Orange, NJ 07052
Optometrist, homeopathic physician, lecturer, research scientist, author

Beals, Leroy Vaughn, Jr.
3700 W. Juneau Ave.
Milwaukee, WI 53208
President and CEO,
Harley Davidson Motor Co., Inc.

Bean, Orson (Dallas Frederick Burrows)
c/o The Gage Group
9229 W. Sunset Blvd.
Los Angeles, CA 90069
Actor, comedian

The Beastie Boys
c/o Russell Simmons,
Rush Productions
298 Elizabeth St.
New York, NY 10012
Rap group

Beatlemania
P.O. Box 262
Carteret, NJ 07008
Beatles sound-alike group

Beaton, Roy Howard
175 Curtner Ave.
San Jose, CA 95125
Nuclear industries executive

Beatrice Companies, Inc.
2 N. La Salle St.
Chicago, IL 60602
Donald P. Kelly,
chairman of the board and CEO

Beatty, Ned
9250 Sunset Blvd., Suite 1105
Los Angeles, CA 90069
Actor

Beatty, Warren
1849 Sawtelle, Suite 500
Los Angeles, CA 90069
Actor

Beaver, Donald L., Jr.
2614 18th St.
Altoona, PA 16601
President and cofounder,
The New Pig Corp., company that makes tubular "socks" to absorb fluid leaks

Beaver, Paul Chester
1430 Tulane Ave.
New Orleans, LA 70112
Parasitologist

Bechtel Group, Inc.
50 Beale St.
San Francisco, CA 94105
Stephen D. Bechtel, Jr.,
chairman of the board

Becker, Boris
c/o U.S. Tennis Association
51 E. 42nd St.
New York, NY 10017
Tennis player

Becker, George James
1720 South Shores Rd.
San Diego, CA 92109
President, Sea World, Inc.

Becker, Robert Jerome
730 Springer Dr.
Lombard, IL 60148
Allergist, health care consultant

Beckett, Samuel
c/o Farber & Farber
3 Queen St.
London WC1 England
Nobel Prize–winning writer

Beech Aircraft Corp.
9709 E. Central
Wichita, KS 67206
*James S. Walsh,
president and CEO*

The Bee Gees
c/o Borman-Sternberg Entertainment
9220 Sunset Blvd., Suite 320
Los Angeles, CA 90069
Singing group

Beekman, Phillip G.
375 Park Ave.
New York, NY 10152
*President,
Joseph Seagram & Sons, Inc.*

Beerman, Herman
2422 Pine St.
Philadelphia, PA 19103
Physician, editor

Beery, Noah
c/o The Mishkin Agency
9255 Sunset Blvd.
Los Angeles, CA 90069
Actor

Begley, Ed, Jr.
c/o MTM Productions
4024 Radford Ave.
Studio City, CA 91604
Producer, actor

Belafonte, Harry
P.O. Box 1700, Ansonia Station
New York, NY 10023
Singer, actor

Bel Geddes, Barbara
3970 Overland Ave.
Culver City, CA 90230
Actress

Belkin, Boris David
c/o International Creative
Management
40 W. 57th St.
New York, NY 10019
Violinist

Bell, Buddy (David Gus Bell)
Cincinnati Reds
100 Riverfront Stadium
Cincinnati, OH 45202
Baseball player

Bell & Howell Co.
5215 Old Orchard Rd.
Skokie, IL 60077-1076
Donald N. Frey,
chairman of the board and CEO

Bellamy, Ralph
116 E. 27th St.
New York, NY 10016
Actor

Bellocchi, Natale H.
c/o U.S. State Department,
Botswana Post
Washington, DC 20520
U.S. ambassador to Botswana

Belt, Edward Scudder
123 Pratt Museum
Amherst College
Amherst, MA 01002
Sedimentologist, educator

Belushi, James
1888 Century Park E., Suite 1400
Los Angeles, CA 90067
Actor

**Benatar, Pat
(Pat Andrejewski)**
c/o Premier Talent Agency
3 E. 54th St.
New York, NY 10022
Rock singer

Bench, Johnny
105 E. 4th St., Suite 800
Cincinnati, OH 45202
Retired baseball player

Benchley, Peter
c/o International Creative
Management
40 W. 57th St.
New York, NY 10019
Author

Bendjedid, Chadli
Office of the President
Algiers, Algeria
President of Algeria

Benedict, Alvin
3645 Las Vegas Blvd. S.
Las Vegas, NV 90230
Chairman and CEO,
MGM Grand Hotels, Inc.

Benedict, Dirk
9000 Sunset Blvd., Number 1112
Los Angeles, CA 90069
Actor

Benedict, Paul
409 N. Camden Dr.
Number 202
Beverly Hills, CA 90210
Actor

Beneficial Corp.
1100 Carr Rd.
Wilmington, DE 19809
Finn M. W. Caspersen, CEO

Benjamin, Richard
222 N. Canon Dr.
Beverly Hills, CA 90210
Actor

**Bennett, Harve
(Harve Fischman)**
c/o Paramount Pictures
5555 Melrose Ave.
Los Angeles, CA 90038
Producer

Bennett, William John
Office of the Secretary,
Dept. of Education
400 Maryland Ave.
SW. Washington, DC 20202
*Secretary, U.S. Department of
Education*

Benson, George
151 El Camino Dr.
Beverly Hills, CA 90212
Guitarist, songwriter

Benson, Warren Frank
c/o Eastman School of Music,
U. of Rochester
26 Gibbs St.
Rochester, NY 14604
Composer, educator

Benton, Barbi
P.O. Box 7114
Pasadena, CA 91109
Actress

Benton, Connie
P.O. Box 50304
Washington, DC 20004
Singer

Benton, Robert
c/o International Creative
Management
40 W. 57th St.
New York, NY 10019
Screenwriter, director

Beradino, John
c/o ABC-TV Press Relations
1330 Ave. of the Americas
New York, NY 10019
Actor

Berenger, Tom
P.O. Box 1842
Beaufort, SC 29901-1842
Actor

Beresford, Bruce
151 El Camino Dr.
Beverly Hills, CA 90212
Motion picture director

Berger, Richard L.
10202 W. Washington Blvd.
Culver City, CA 90232
*President,
Metro-Goldwyn-Mayer/United
Artists*

Bergman, Alan
c/o Freedman, Kinzelberg &
Broder
1801 Ave. of the Stars
Los Angeles, CA 90067
Wrote lyrics to "Ol' MacDonald"

Bergman, Ingmar
P.O. Box 27127 S-10252
Stockholm, Sweden
08/630510
Motion picture writer and director

Bergman, Jules
c/o ABC News
7 W. 66th St.
New York, NY 10023
ABC News science correspondent

Bergman, Sandahl
445 N. Bedford Dr.
Beverly Hills, CA 90210
Actress

**Berle, Milton
(Milton Berlinger)**
151 El Camino Dr.
Beverly Hills, CA 90212
Actor, comedian

Berlin
c/o Perry Watts-Russell,
MFC Management
1830 S. Robertson, Number 201
Los Angeles, CA 90035
Pop music group

Berlin, Irving
1290 6th Ave.
New York, NY 10104
Composer

Berman, Pandro Samuel
914 N. Roxbury Dr.
Beverly Hills, CA 90210
Motion picture producer

Bernays, Edward L.
7 Lowell St.
Cambridge, MA 02138
Public relations council, touted "Father" of modern PR

Bernhard, Sandra
11353 W. Olympic Blvd.
Suite 3500
Los Angeles, CA 90064
Entertainer

Bernstein, Carl
c/o International Creative
Management
40 W. 57th St.
New York, NY 10019
Journalist, author

Bernstein, Leonard
Amerson Enterprises
24 W. 57th St.
New York, NY 10019
Conductor, pianist, composer

**Berra, Yogi
(Lawrence Peter Berra)**
P.O. Box 288
Houston, TX 77001
Baseball coach

Berry, Chuck (Charles Edward Anderson Berry)
691 Buckner Rd.
Wentzville, MO 63385
Rock guitarist, songwriter

Berry, Ken
c/o STE Representation Ltd.
211 S. Beverly Dr., Suite 201
Beverly Hills, CA 90212
Actor

HRH Prince Bertil
Hertigens av Halland
Kungl Slottet
11130 Stockholm, Sweden

Bertinelli, Valerie
10350 Santa Monica Blvd.
Suite 350
Los Angeles, CA 90067
Actress

Bertolucci, Bernardo
Vai Del Babuino 51
Rome, Italy
Motion picture director

Best, James Knowland
1901 Ave. of the Stars, Suite 500
Los Angeles, CA 90067
Actor

Bestor, Charles Lemon
c/o U. of Massachusetts,
Dept. of Music
Amherst, MA 01002
Composer, educator

Best Sausage, Inc.
5110 E. Washington
Las Vegas, NV 89110
Robert Best, president. Makers of the best sausage

Bethlehem Steel Corp.
Martin Tower
Bethlehem, PA 18016
Walter F. Williams, president and CEO

Betts, Dicky (Richard Forrest Betts)
c/o International Creative Management
40 W. 57th St.
New York, NY 10019
Guitarist, songwriter, vocalist

B-52's
c/o Martin Kirkup,
Direct Management Group
945A N. La Cienega
Los Angeles, CA 90069
Pop music group

Bharati, Agehananda
500 University Pl.
Syracuse, NY 13244
Anthropologist, Hindu monk, educator, author

Bic Corp.
Wiley St.
Milford, CT 06460
Bruno Bich, president

Biederman, Charles Joseph
Route 2
Red Wing, MN 55006
Artist

Big Bird
c/o Children's Television Workshop
One Lincoln Plaza
New York, NY 10023
Sesame Street *character*

Biniger, Clem Edward
c/o First Presbyterian Church
401 SE. 15th Ave. at Terpon Bend
Fort Lauderdale, FL 33301
Clergyman

Binkerd, Gordon Ware
c/o Boosey & Hawkes, Inc.
24 W. 57th St.
New York, NY 10019
Composer

Bird, Larry
c/o Boston Celtics
Boston Station
Boston, MA 02114
Basketball player

Biscardi, Chester
542 Ave. of the Americas
Suite 4R
New York, NY 10011
Composer

Bishop, Jim
641 West Dr.
Delray Beach, FL 33445
Author

Bishop, Stephen
c/o Trudy Green Management
1800 Marcheeta Pl.
Los Angeles, CA 90069
Singer, songwriter

Bisset, Jacqueline
c/o International Creative Management
40 W. 57th St.
New York, NY 10019
Actress

Black, Karen
9255 Sunset Blvd., Suite 509
Los Angeles, CA 90069
Actress

Black, Shirley Temple
115 Lakewood Dr.
Woodside, CA 94062
Former actress, former U.S. ambassador

Black & Decker Corp.
701 E. Joppa Rd.
Towson, MD 21204
Nolan D. Archibald, president and CEO

Blackstone, Harry
c/o David Belenzon Management
Box 15428
San Diego, CA 92115
Magician, actor

Blackwood, James Webre
5180 Park Ave.
Memphis, TN 38117
Gospel singer, clergyman

Blackwood, Nina
16161 Ventura Blvd., Suite 714
Encino, CA 91436
Television personality

Blaine, Nell Walden
3 Ledge Rd.
Gloucester, MA 01930
Painter

Blair, Linda
8730 Sunset Dr., 6th Floor
Los Angeles, CA 90069
Actress

Blair, William Draper, Jr.
1800 N. Kent St.
Arlington, VA 22209
Conservationist

Blake, Ran
c/o New England Conservatory
290 Huntington Ave.
Boston, MA 02115
Jazz pianist, composer

Blanc, Frederic C.
220 Huntington Plaza
Northeastern University
Boston, MA 02115
Professor, expert in industrial waste

Blanc, Mel
9454 Wilshire Blvd.
Beverly Hills, CA 90212
Cartoon character voiceover artist

Blanchard, James J.
Office of the Governor
State Capitol
Lansing, MI 48909
Governor of Michigan

Blanchard, Nina
7060 Hollywood Blvd., Suite 1010
Los Angeles, CA 90028
Modeling agent

Bland, Bobby Blue
3500 W. Olive Ave., Number 740
Burbank, CA 91505-4628
Blues singer, guitarist

Blane, John
c/o American Embassy
BP413
N'Djamena, Chad
U.S. ambassador to Chad

**Blass, Bill
(William Ralph Blass)**
c/o Bill Blass Ltd.
550 7th Ave.
New York, NY 10018
Creator of designer apparel and home furnishings

Blatt, Burton
150 Huntington Hall
Syracuse University
Syracuse, NY 13210
University dean, educator

Bley, Paul
P.O. Box 225
Village Station, NY 10014
Jazz pianist, composer, producer

Bloch, Henry Wollman
4410 Main St.
Kansas City, MO 64111
President, CEO, and director,
H & R Block, Inc.

Bloch, Robert
c/o Shapiro-Lichtman Talent
Agency
8827 Beverly Blvd.
Los Angeles, CA 90067
Author, motion picture and
television writer

Block, Lawrence
39 1/2 Washington Square S.
New York, NY 10012
Author

Bloom, Claire
9255 Sunset Blvd., Suite 505
Los Angeles, CA 90069
Actress

Bloom, Jake
9255 Sunset Blvd., 10th Floor
Los Angeles, CA 90069
Theatrical attorney

Bloom, Lindsay
Box 2188
Hollywood, CA 90078
Actress

Bloomingdale's Dept. Stores
7 W. 7th St.
Cincinnati, OH 45202
Howard Goldfeder,
chairman and CEO

Blount, Melvin Cornell
Three Rivers Stadium
Pittsburgh, PA 15212
Football player

Blue, Vida
P.O. Box 14438
Oakland, CA 94614-2438
Baseball player

Blue Grass Breeders, Inc.
7720 E. Bellview Ave.
Englewood, CO 80111
Douglas A. Sykes, president.
Company breeds and races
Thoroughbred horses

Bly, Robert Elwood
308 1st St.
Moose Lake, MN 55767
Poet

Bob, The Big Boy
505 Mitchell Ave.
Syracuse, NY 13211
Hamburger spokesboy

Bobko, Karol J.
c/o NASA Johnson Space Center
Houston, TX 77058
*Astronaut, pilot for first space
shuttle mission*

Bob & Ray
420 Lexington Ave.
New York, NY 10021
Comedy team

Bochco, Steve
4024 Radford Ave.
Studio City, CA 91604
Television producer, screenwriter

Boehm, Richard Wood
U.S. Ambassador to Cyprus
c/o U.S. State Department
Washington, DC 20520
U.S. ambassador to Cyprus

The Boeing Company
7755 E. Marginal Way S.
Seattle, WA 98124
*T. A. Wilson,
chairman of the board and CEO*

Boeker, Paul Harold
U.S. Embassy Amman
APO New York, NY 09892
U.S. ambassador to Jordan

Bogdanovich, Peter
c/o Camp & Peiffer
2040 Ave. of the Stars
Century City, CA 90067
*Motion picture producer and
director*

Bohay, Heidi
c/o The Gage Group
9229 Sunset Blvd.
Los Angeles, CA 90069
Actress

Boise Cascade Corp.
One Jefferson Sq.
Boise, ID 83728
*John B. Fery,
chairman of the board and CEO*

Boles, Roger
c/o UC San Francisco,
Dept. of Otolaryngology
400 Parnassus Ave., Suite 739A
San Francisco, CA 94122
Otolaryngologist

Bolger, Ray
618 N. Beverly Dr.
Beverly Hills, CA 90210
Actor

Bologna, Joseph
10000 Santa Monica Blvd.
Suite 305
Los Angeles, CA 90067
Actor

Bombeck, Erma
1703 Kaiser Ave.
Irvine, CA 92714
Author, columnist

Bon Jovi
c/o McGhee Entertainment
240 Central Park S., Suite 2C
New York, NY 10019
Rock group

THE ADDRESS BOOK

Bono, Sonny Salvatore
1700 N. Indian Ave.
Palm Springs, CA 92262
Singer, composer, actor

The Boomtown Rats
44 Seymour
London W1 England
Rock band

Boone, Debby
15315 Magnolia Blvd.
Sherman Oaks, CA 91403
Singer

**Boone, Pat
(Charles Eugene Boone)**
9255 Sunset Blvd., Suite 519
Los Angeles, CA 90069
Singer, actor

Boorman, John
c/o Edgar Gross
1801 Century Park E., Suite 1132
Los Angeles, CA 90067
*Motion picture writer, producer,
director*

Boorstin, Daniel J.
c/o Library of Congress
Washington, DC 20540
Author, government official

Bordallo, Madeleine Mary
P.O. Box 1458
Agana, GU 96910
First Lady of Guam

Borden, Inc.
277 Park Ave.
New York, NY 10172
Eugene J. Sullivan, CEO

Borg, Bjorn
Liestoire Ave.
Princess Grace
Monte Carlo, Monaco
Tennis player

Borge, Victor
c/o International Creative
Management
40 W. 57th St.
New York, NY 10019
Comedian, pianist

Borgnine, Ernest
132 Lasky Dr.
Beverly Hills, CA 90212
Actor

Borowitz, Eugene B.
P.O. Box 567
Port Washington, NY 11050
*Editor of Sh'ma, a journal of
Jewish responsibility*

Borsari, Peter C.
7650 Curson Terrace
Los Angeles, CA 90046
Theatrical photographer

Bosco, Philip Michael
c/o Hesseltine Baker Ltd.
165 W. 46th St.
New York, NY 10036
Actor

48

Bosley, Tom
113 San Vicente Blvd., Suite 202
Beverly Hills, CA 90211
Actor

Boston
c/o Jeff Dorenfeld
1560 Trapelo Rd.
Waltham, MA 02154
Rock group

Bostwick, Barry
151 El Camino Dr.
Beverly Hills, CA 90212
Actor

Bosworth, Stephen Warren
c/o U.S. Embassy
APO San Francisco, CA 96528
U.S. ambassador to Philippines

Botha, Pieter W.
Union Bldng.
Pretoria 0001, Republic of South
Africa
President of South Africa

Bottoms, Timothy
15760 Ventura Blvd., Suite 1730
Encino, CA 91436
Actor

Bourque, Pierre
4101 E. Sherbrooke St.
Montreal PQ H1X 2B2
Canada
Horticulturist

**Bowie, David
(David Robert Jones)**
641 5th Ave., Suite 22Q
New York, NY 10022
Musician, actor

Boxcar Willie
1300 Division St., Number 103
Nashville, TN 37203
Country singer

Boy George (George-O'Dowd)
153 George St.
London W1 England
Pop singer

Boylan, John Patrick
1801 Century Park W.
Los Angeles, CA 90067
Record producer, songwriter

Boyle, Peter
c/o Robbins & Steilman
1700 Broadway
New York, NY 10019
Actor

Bozo The Clown
5455 Wilshire Blvd., Suite 2200
Los Angeles, CA 90036
Jerry Digney

**Bracken, Eddie
(Edward Vincent)**
215 S. La Cienega Blvd., Suite 200
Beverly Hills, CA 90211
Actor, writer, director, singer, artist

Bradbury, Ray
c/o Bantam Books
666 5th Ave.
New York, NY 10103
Author

Bradford, Barbara Taylor
450 Park Ave.
New York, NY 10022
Journalist, author, novelist

Bradley, Ed
c/o CBS News
524 W. 57th St.
New York, NY 10019
*News correspondent,
CBS's 60 Minutes*

Bradley, Thomas
Office of the Mayor
City Hall
Los Angeles, CA 90012
Mayor of Los Angeles

Bradshaw, Terry
P.O. Box 1607
Shreveport, LA 71165
Football player

Brady, Ray
c/o CBS News
524 W. 57th St.
New York, NY 10019
Business and financial commentator, CBS Morning News

Brady, Scott
8150 Beverly Blvd., Suite 206
Los Angeles, CA 90048
Actor

Branagan, Laura
9000 Sunset Blvd., Suite 1200
Los Angeles, CA 90069
Singer

Branch, Clifford
332 Center St.
El Segundo, CA 90245
Football player

Brand, Neville
8899 Beverly Blvd.
Los Angeles, CA 90048
Actor

Brando, Marlon, Jr.
c/o Browncraft
11940 San Vicente Blvd.
Los Angeles, CA 90049
Actor

Braniff Airlines
7701 Lemmon Ave.
Dallas, TX 75209
*Jay A. Pritzker,
chairman of the board and CEO*

Braun, Matitiahu
Avery Fisher Hall
Lincoln Center
New York, NY 10023
Violinist, violist

Braun, Zev
291 S. La Cienega Blvd.
Penthouse 33
Beverly Hills, CA 90211
Motion picture producer

Braverman, Charles Dell
8899 Beverly Blvd.
Los Angeles, CA 90048
Motion picture producer, director

Brennan, Eileen
1888 Century Park E., Suite 1400
Los Angeles, CA 90067
Actress

Brennan, William Joseph, Jr.
c/o Supreme Court of the
United States
Washington, DC 20543
U.S. Supreme Court justice

Brenner, David
c/o International Creative
Management
40 W. 57th St.
New York, NY 10019
Comedian

Brett, George
P.O. Box 1969
Kansas City, MO 64141
Baseball player

**Brickhouse, Jack
(John B. Brickhouse)**
2501 W. Bradley Pl.
Chicago, IL 60618
*Radio and television sports
announcer, author*

**Bridges, Beau
(Lloyd Vernet Bridges III)**

1888 Century Park E., Suite 1400
Los Angeles, CA 90067
Actor

Bridges, James
1888 Century Park E., Suite 1400
Los Angeles, CA 90067
Motion picture writer and director

Bridges, Jeff
1888 Century Park E., Suite 1400
Los Angeles, CA 90067
Actor

Bridges, Lloyd
151 El Camino Dr.
Beverly Hills, CA 90212
Actor

Brinkley, David
c/o ABC News
1717 DeSales St. NW.
Washington, DC 20036
News commentator

Brinks, Inc.
Thorndal Circle
Darien, CT 06820-1225
*D. L. Marshall, chairman of the
board and CEO. Armored car
service*

Brisco-Hooks, Valerie
P.O. Box 21053
Long Beach, CA 90801
Olympic track and field athlete

Bristol-Meyers Co.
345 Park Ave.
New York, NY 10154
Richard L. Gelb,
chairman of the board and CEO

Brittany, Morgan
18060 Boris Dr.
Encino, CA 91316
Actress

Broccoli, Albert Romolo
1900 Ave. of the Stars, Suite 535
Los Angeles, CA 90067
Producer of James Bond films

Brock, Karena Diane
2212 Lincoln St.
Savannah, GA 31401
Ballerina

Brock Candy Co.
4120 Jersy Pike
Chattanooga, TN 37422-2474
Paul K. Brock, president and CEO

Brodie, John Riley
c/o NBC Sports Press Dept.
30 Rockefeller Plaza
New York, NY 10112
Television sportscaster, former
football player

Brokaw, Norman
151 El Camino Dr.
Beverly Hills, CA 90212

COB, William Morris Agency
(an entertainer's management
company)

Brokaw, Tom
c/o NBC News
30 Rockefeller Plaza
New York, NY 10112
Journalist

Brolin, James
8899 Beverly Blvd.
Los Angeles, CA 90048
Actor

Bronson, Charles
(Charles Buchinsky)
9169 Sunset Blvd.
Los Angeles, CA 90069
Actor

Brooks, Albert
c/o Moress-Nanas Entertainment
2128 Pico Blvd.
Santa Monica, CA 90405
Actor, writer, director

Brooks, Mel
P.O. Box 900
Beverly Hills, CA 90213
Director, writer, actor

Brothers, Dr. Joyce
c/o New York Post
210 South St.
New York, NY 10002
Psychologist

Broussard, John
Box 190
Kapaau, HI 96755
Owner, Rainbow Ridge, a company that sells an address list of women who seek the perfect mate

Brower, David Ross
c/o Friends of Earth Society
1045 Sansome St.
San Francisco, CA 94111
Conservationist

Brown, David
c/o Zanuck/Brown Co.
200 W. 57th St.
New York, NY 10019
Motion picture producer

Brown, Earle
c/o ICI
799 Broadway
New York, NY 10003
Composer, conductor

Brown, Edmund Gerald, Jr. (Jerry)
11500 W. Olympic Blvd.
Suite 302
Los Angeles, CA 90064
Former governor of California

Brown, Edmund Gerald, Sr. (Pat)
450 N. Roxbury Dr.
Beverly Hills, CA 90210
Former governor of California

Brown, Jack Harold Upton
c/o University of Houston
4800 Calhoun St.
Houston, TX 77004
Biomedical engineer, university official, educator

Brown, James
c/o Brothers Management Associates
141 Dunbar Ave.
Fords, NJ 08863
Soul singer

Brown, Jim
2040 Ave. of the Stars, 4th Floor
Los Angeles, CA 90067
Former football player, actor

Brown, William A.
c/o U.S. Embassy
95 Wireless Rd.
Bangkok, Thailand
U.S. ambassador to Thailand

Browne, Dik
c/o King Features Syndicate
245 E. 45th St.
New York, NY 10017
Cartoonist, creator of "Hager The Horrible"

Browne, Jackson
1888 Century Park E., Suite 1400
Los Angeles, CA 90028
Singer, songwriter

Browne, Leslie
c/o American Ballet Theatre
890 Broadway
New York, NY 10003
Dancer, actress

Browne, Roscoe Lee
c/o Georgia Gilly
8721 Sunset Blvd.
Los Angeles, CA 90069
Actor, director, writer

Browne, Walter Shawn
8 Parnassus Rd.
Berkeley, CA 94708
Chess player, journalist

Browning, The Right Reverend Edmund Lee
815 2nd Ave.
New York, NY 10017
Presiding bishop of the Episcopal Church

Broyhill Furniture Co.
Highway 321 By-Pass
Lenoir, NC 28645
*Paul H. Broyhill,
chairman of the board*

Brubeck, David
c/o Derry Music Co.
601 Montgomery St.
San Francisco, CA 94111
Musician

Brusilow, Anshel
4545 Laren Ln.
Dallas, TX 75234
Conductor

Bryan, Richard H.
Office of Governor, Capitol Complex
Carson City, NV 89710
Governor of Nevada

Bryant, Anita
P.O. Box 899
Selma, AL 36701
Entertainer

Brzezinski, Zbigniew
c/o Columbia University School of Government
New York, NY 10027
Author, former head of the National Security Council

Buchanan, John Donald
U.S. Regulatory Commission
Washington, DC 20555
Radiochemist, health physicist

Buchwald, Art
2000 Pennsylvania Ave.
NW. Washington, DC 20006
Columnist, author

Buckingham, Lindsey
3389 Camino de la Cumbre
Sherman Oaks, CA 91423
Rock musician, songwriter

Buck Knives, Inc.
1900 Weld Blvd.
El Cajon, CA 92022
*Alfred C. Buck,
chairman of the board*

Buckley, Emerson
1430 N. Federal Highway
Fort Lauderdale, FL 33304
Conductor, music director

Buckley, William Frank, Jr.
150 E. 35th St.
New York, NY 10016
*Conservative columnist, magazine
editor, commentator*

Buckner, William J.
c/o Boston Red Sox
Fenway Park
Boston, MA 02215
Baseball player

Bucy, Paul C.
P.O. Box 1457
Tryon, NC 28782
Neurological surgeon

Budd, Zola
One Church Row
Wandsworth Plain
London SW18 England
Olympic runner

Budget Rent-A-Car Corp.
200 N. Michigan Ave.
Chicago, IL 60601
*Morris Belzberg,
president and CEO*

Buffalo Bill Fur Salon
1507 8th St.
Cody, WY 82414
*Claud E. Brown. Retail furriers
and apartment building operators*

Buffet, Jimmy
1888 Century Park E., Suite 1400
Los Angeles, CA 90067
Singer, songwriter, musician

Buffkins, Archie Lee
Executive Suite
Kennedy Center
Washington, DC 20566
Performing arts administrator

Buffums, Inc.
301 Long Beach Blvd.
Long Beach, CA 90802
*Robert J. Hampson,
president and CEO*

Bugliosi, Vincent
9300 Wilshire Blvd., Number 470
Beverly Hills, CA 90210
*Prosecuting attorney in Manson
trial*

**Bullocks Department
Stores**
7 W. 7th St.
Cincinnati, OH 45202
*Howard Goldfeder,
chairman and CEO*

**Bunce, Donald Fairburn
MacDougal II**
404 Woodland Hills
Tuscaloosa, AL 35405
Anatomist, physician

Bunim, Mary Ellis
524 W. 57th St.
New York, NY 10019
Television producer

Burger, Warren Earl
U.S. Supreme Court Bldg.
Washington, DC 20543
Supreme Court justice

Burger King Corp.
7360 N. Kendall Dr.
Miami, FL 33152
J. Jeffery Campbell,
chairman of the board and CEO

Burgess, Anthony
44 Rue Grimaldi
Monte Carlo, Monaco
Author

Burgess, William Henry
550 Palisades Dr.
Palm Springs, CA 92262
Financier

Burke, Delta
c/o CBS Television City
7800 Beverly Blvd.
Los Angeles, CA 90036
Actress

Burlington Industries, Inc.
3330 W. Friendly Ave.
Greensboro, NC 27410
William A. Klopman,
chairman of the board and CEO

Burnett, Carol
8899 Beverly Blvd.
Los Angeles, CA 90048
Actress, comedienne

Burns, Allan P.
4024 Radford Ave.
Studio City, CA 91604
Writer, television producer

Burns, George
c/o Irving Fine
1100 N. Alta Loma Rd.
Los Angeles, CA 90069
Comedian

Burr, Raymond
c/o Dennis-Karg-Dennis & Co.
470 San Vicente Blvd.
Los Angeles, CA 90048
Actor

Burroughs, William S.
c/o Grove Press, Inc.
196 W. Houston St.
New York, NY 10014
Writer

Burroughs Corp.
Burroughs Pl.
Detroit, MI 48232
W. Michael Blumenthal,
chairman of the board and CEO

Burrows, Victoria
7083 Hollywood Blvd., 3rd Floor
Los Angeles, CA 90028
Casting director

Burstyn, Ellen
(Edna Rae Gillooly)
P.O. Box 217
Palisades, NY 10964-0271
Actress

**Burton, Levar
(Levardis Robert Martyn, Jr.)**
c/o Delores Robinson Management
7319 Beverly Blvd.
Los Angeles, CA 90036
Actor

Busey, Gary
c/o Moress-Nanas Entertainment
2128 Pico Blvd.
Santa Monica, CA 90405
Actor, musician

Bush, Barbara Pierce
The Vice President's House
Washington, DC 20501
Wife of George Bush

Bush, George Herbert Walker
White House
1600 Pennsylvania Ave.
Washington, DC 20501
Vice president of the United States

Bush, Irving M.
Chapman Rd.
Burlington, IL 60109
Urological surgeon

Butler, Len
17 Battery Place
New York, NY 10004
President, Meter Advertising Corp., a company that places advertising on parking meters

Button, Richard
250 W. 57th St., Suite 1818
New York, NY 10107
Television producer, former figure skating champion

By-Products Corp.
132 St. Clair Ave.
East St. Louis, IL 62201
Joseph Folberg, chairman of the board. Wholesale animal by-products

Byrd, Robert C.
c/o United States Senate Offices
Washington, DC 20501
U.S. senator

Byrne, David
c/o Index Music
1775 Broadway
New York, NY 10019
Musician, composer, artist, director

Caan, James
10100 Santa Monica Blvd.
16th Floor
Los Angeles, CA 90067
Actor, director

Caen, Herb
c/o San Francisco Chronicle
Publishing Co.
925 Mission St.
San Francisco, CA 94103
Newspaper columnist, author

Caesar, Sid
c/o Korman Contemporary Artists Ltd.
132 Lasky Dr.
Beverly Hills, CA 90212
Actor, comedian

Caesar's World, Inc.
1801 Century Park E.
Los Angeles, CA 90067
Henry Gluck,
chairman of the board and CEO

Cahn, Sammy
2049 Century Park E., Suite 2500
Los Angeles, CA 90067
Lyric songwriter

Caldwell, Erskine
c/o McIntosh & Otis, Inc.
475 5th Ave.
New York, NY 10017
Author

Calhoun, Noah Robert
c/o Howard University Dental
College
Washington, DC 20059
Oral maxillofacial surgeon,
educator

Calhoun, Rory
c/o Dale Garrick International
Agency
8831 Sunset Blvd.
Los Angeles, CA 90069
Actor, director, producer, writer

**California State Lottery
Headquarters**
P.O. Box 3028
Sacramento, CA 95812

Caliguiri, Richard S.
Office of Mayor, City Hall
414 Grand St.
Pittsburgh, PA 15219
Mayor of Pittsburgh

Calloway, Cab
1040 Knollwood Rd.
White Plains, NY 10603
Blues singer

Calvo, Paul MacDonald
Office of the Governor
Agana, GU 96910
Governor of Guam

Cameo
1422 Teach St., Suite 300
Atlanta, GA 30390
Funk group

Cameron, Kirk
P.O. Box 2592
Hollywood, CA 90078
Actor

Camp, Joseph Shelton, Jr.
10300 N. Central Expressway 100
Dallas, TX 75231
Producer of "Benji" films

Campbell, Allan Barrie
195 Dafoe Rd.
Winnipeg MB R3T 2M9
Canada
Plant breeder

Campbell, Earl
1500 Poydras St.
New Orleans, LA 70112
Football player

Campbell, Glen
9200 Sunset Blvd., Suite 823
Los Angeles, CA 90069
Singer, entertainer

Campbell Soup Co.
Campbell Pl.
Camden, NJ 08103
*John T. Dorrance, Jr.,
chairman of the board*

Campus, Peter
c/o Paula Cooper Gallery
155 Wooster St.
New York, NY 10012
Video artist

Caniff, Milton Arthur
c/o King Features Syndicate
235 E. 45th St.
New York, NY 10017
Cartoonist

Cannell, Stephen Joseph
7083 Hollywood Blvd.
Los Angeles, CA 90028
*Television writer, producer,
director*

Cannon, Dyan
1888 Century Park E., Suite 1400
Los Angeles, CA 90067
Actress

Cannon, J.D.
c/o The Artists Agency
190 N. Canon Dr.
Beverly Hills, CA 90210
Actor

Cannon Group, Inc.
6464 Sunset Blvd.
Los Angeles, CA 90028
Menahem Golan,
chairman of the board

Canova, Diana
10100 Santa Monica Blvd., 16th
Floor
Los Angeles, CA 90067
Actress

Capelli, John Placido
35 Kings Highway
Haddonfield, NJ 08033
Nephrologist

Capital Cities/ABC, Inc.
24 E. 51st St.
New York, NY 10022
Thomas S. Murphy,
chairman of the board and CEO

Capo, Fran
85-20 167th St.
Jamaica, NY 11432
Comedienne, radio writer, holds
world record for fast talking:
585 words per minute

Capra, Frank
P.O. Box 980
La Quinta, CA 92253
Motion picture producer, director

Capra, Tom
c/o ABC Public Relations
1330 Ave. of the Americas
New York, NY 10019
Television producer

Capshaw, Kate
1888 Century Park E., Suite 1400
Los Angeles, CA 90067
Actress

Captain and Tennille
(Daryl and Toni Dragon)
P.O. Box 262
Glenbrook, NV 89413-0262
Entertainers

Cara, Irene
8033 Sunset Blvd., Number 735
Los Angeles, CA 90046
Actress

Caras, Roger Andrew
46 Fenmarsh Rd.
East Hampton, NY 11937
Motion picture company exec.,
author

Caray, Harry
c/o Chicago Cubs, Wrigley Field
Chicago, IL 60613
Sports announcer

Cardin, Pierre
59 Rue De Faubourg Saint-Ho-
nore
75008 Paris, France
Fashion designer

Carew, Rod
2000 State College Blvd.
Anaheim, CA 92806
Former baseball player

Carey, Harry, Jr.
4513 Vista Del Monte
Sherman Oaks, CA 91403
Actor

Carey, MacDonald
c/o NBC Press Dept.
30 Rockefeller Plaza
New York, NY 10112
Actor

Carey, Ron
c/o Four D Productions
1438 N. Gower St.
Hollywood, CA 90028
Actor

Carlin, George
901 Bringham Ave.
Los Angeles, CA 90049
Comedian

Carlin, John William
Officer of Governor
State House
Topeka, KS 66612
Governor of Kansas

Carlisle, Belinda
c/o Gold Spaceship
3575 Cahuenga W., Suite 470
Los Angeles, CA 90068
Singer, recording artist

King Juan Carlos
Palacio de la Carcuela
Madrid, Spain
King of Spain

Carl's Jr.
1200 N. Harbor Blvd.
Anaheim, CA 92801
Carl N. Karcher,
chairman of the board and CEO

Carner, Joanne Gunderson
1250 Shoreline Dr., Suite 200
Sugar Land, TX 77478
Golfer

Carnes, Kim
c/o Ken Kragen
1112 N. Sherbourne Dr.
Los Angeles, CA 90069
Rock singer

Carney, Art (Arthur William Mathew Carney)
RR 20 Box 911
Westbrook, CT 06498
Actor

Carney, Patricia
House of Commons Room 440-N
Center Block Parliament Bldgs.
Ottawa, ON. K1A 0A6
Canada
Canadian minister of energy,
mines, and resources

Princess Caroline
Grimaldi Palace
Monte Carlo, Monaco
Princess of Monaco

Carpenter, John
8383 Wilshire Blvd., Suite 840
Beverly Hills, CA 90211
Motion picture writer, director

Carr, Alan
439 N. Bedford Dr., Suite 1000
Beverly Hills, CA 90210
Theatrical producer

Carr, Martin Douglas
305 W. 86th St.
New York, NY 10024
Television producer, director, writer

Carr, Vikki
c/o Arnold Mills, VI-CAR
Enterprises, Inc.
8961 Sunset Blvd.
Los Angeles, CA 90069
Singer

Carradine, David
8899 Beverly Blvd.
Los Angeles, CA 90048
Actor

Carradine, John
c/o Ruth Webb Enterprises
7500 Devista Dr.
Los Angeles, CA 90046
Actor

Carradine, Keith
151 El Camino Dr.
Beverly Hills, CA 90212
Actor, singer, composer

Carrera, Barbara
1707 Clearview Dr.
Beverly Hills, CA 90210
Actress

Carroll, Diahann
c/o Aaron Spelling Productions
1041 N. Formosa Ave.
Los Angeles, CA 90046
Actress, singer

Carroll, Vinnette Justine
227 W. 17th St., Ground Floor
New York, NY 10011
Actress, stage director, writer

The Cars
331 Newbury St.
Boston, MA 02115
Pop music group

Carson, Johnny
c/o NBC-TV
3000 W. Alameda Ave.
Burbank, CA 91523
Host, The Tonight Show

**Carter, Betty
(Lillie Mae Jones)**
c/o BET-CAR Productions
117 St. Felix St.
Brooklyn, NY 11217
Jazz singer, songwriter

Carter, Clarence Holbrook
Box 119, Route 1
Milford, NJ 08848
Artist

Carter, Gary
c/o NY Mets, Shea Stadium
Roosevelt Ave and 126th St.
Flushing, NY 11368
Baseball player

**Carter, Jimmy
(James Earl Carter, Jr.)**
75 Spring St. SW.
Atlanta, GA 30303
*Former president of the
United States*

Carter, Lynda
151 El Camino Dr.
Beverly Hills, CA 90212
Actress

Carter, Nell
10100 Santa Monica Blvd.
16th Floor
Los Angeles, CA 90067
Actress, singer

Carter, Terry
8300 Santa Monica Blvd.
Suite 203
Los Angeles, CA 90069
Actor, director, producer

Cartland, Barbara
c/o Bantam Books
666 5th Ave.
New York, NY 10103
Author

Cartwright, Veronica
222 N. Canon Dr., Suite 202
Beverly Hills, CA 90210
Actress

Caruba, Alan
P.O. Box 40

Maplewood, NJ 07040
*Founder, The Boring Institute.
Offers information on the boring
things in life*

Casey, Ethel Laughlin
1605 Park Dr.
Raleigh, NC 27605
Opera singer

Casey, Harry Wayne
7764 NW. 71st St.
Miami, FL 33166
*Performer, songwriter, record
producer*

Cash, Johnny
9000 Sunset Blvd., Suite 1200
Los Angeles, CA 90069
Entertainer

Cash, June Carter
c/o CBS Records
51 W. 52nd St.
New York, NY 10019
Singer

Casino Signs, Inc.
4181 W. Oquendo Rd.
Las Vegas, NV 89118
Michael Dean Rogers, president

Cassavetes, John
9056 Santa Monica Blvd.
Suite 201
Los Angeles, CA 90069
Actor

Cassidy, David
8730 Sunset Blvd., 6th Floor
Los Angeles, CA 90069
Actor, singer

Cassidy, Shaun
8899 Beverly Blvd.
Los Angeles, CA 90048
Actor, singer

Castro, Fidel
Palacio del Gobierno
Havana, Cuba
*President and head of
government of Cuba*

Caterpillar, Inc.
100 NE. Adams St.
Peoria, IL 61629
*G. A. Schaefer,
chairman of the board and CEO*

Cavett, Dick
c/o Daphne Productions
228 W. 55th St.
New York, NY 10019
Talk show host

**Cawley, Evonne Goola-
gong**
80 Duntroon Ave.
Roseville, NSW Australia
Tennis player

Cayo, Ronald Jean
c/o Walt Disney Studios
500 S. Buena Vista St.
Burbank, CA 91521

*Motion picture production
company exec.*

CBS, Inc.
51 W. 52nd St.
New York, NY 10019
*Thomas H. Wyman,
president and CEO*

CBS/Fox Video Co.
1211 Ave. of the Americas
New York, NY 10036
*James G. Fitfield,
president and CEO*

Celeste, Richard F.
Office of the Governor, State
Capitol
Columbus, OH 43215
Governor of Ohio

**Century 21 Real Estate
Corp.**
18872 Macarthur Blvd.
Irvine, CA 92715
*Richard J. Loughlin,
president and CEO*

Cessna Aircraft Co.
5800 E. Pawnee Rd.
Wichita, KS 67218
*Russell W. Meyer, Jr.,
chairman of the board*

Cetera, Peter
9200 Sunset Blvd., Suite 915
Los Angeles, CA 90069
Pop singer, songwriter

Cey, Ronald Charles
Wrigley Field
N. Clark and Addison Sts.
Chicago, IL 60613
Baseball player

Chamberlain, Richard
1888 Century Park E., Suite 1400
Los Angeles, CA 90067
Actor

Champion Spark Plug Co.
900 Upton Ave.
Toledo, OH 43607
*Robert A. Stranahan, Jr.,
chairman of the board and CEO*

Chance, Britton
4014 Pine St.
Philadelphia, PA 19104
Educator

Chancellor, John William
c/o NBC-TV
30 Rockefeller Plaza
New York, NY 10112
News correspondent

**Channing, Stockard
(Susan Stockard)**
8899 Beverly Blvd.
Los Angeles, CA 90048
Actress

Chapman, Graham
c/o Monty Python Pictures Ltd.
6-7 Cambridge Gate, 2nd Floor
London NW-1, England
Performer, writer, comedian

Chapman, Mark David
c/o Attica State Prison
Attica, NY 14011
Convicted assassin of John Lennon

Prince Charles
Kensington Palace
London W8 England
Prince of Wales

**Charles, Ray
(Ray Charles Robinson)**
9200 Sunset Blvd., Suite 823
Los Angeles, CA 90069
Musician, singer

Charlie the Tuna
c/o Star-Kist Foods, Inc.
582 Tuna St.
Terminal Island, CA 90731
Spokesfish for Star-Kist Tuna

Charlton, Janet
660 White Plains
Tarrytown, NY 10591
Gossip columnist

Chartoff, Robert Irwin
c/o Chartoff-Winker Productions,
Inc.
10125 W. Washington Blvd.
Culver City, CA 90232
Motion picture producer

Chase, Chevy
8436 W. 3rd St., Suite 650
Los Angeles, CA 90048
Actor, comedian

Chase Manhattan Corp.
One Chase Manhattan Plaza
New York, NY 10018
Willard C. Butcher,
chairman of the board and CEO

Chavez, Cesar
La Paz
Keene, CA 93531
Union official

Cheap Trick
P.O. Box 24640, Village Station
Los Angeles, CA 90024
Rock band

Checker Auto Parts, Inc.
3145 W. Lewis Ave.
Phoenix, AZ 85005
S. Donley Ritchey,
president and CEO

Chemical Bank
277 Park Ave.
New York, NY 10172
Walter V. Shipley,
chairman of the board and CEO

Cheng, Thomas Clement
c/o Marine Biomedical Research
Program
P.O. Box 12559
Charleston, SC 29412
Parasitologist, educator, author

Chennault, Anna Chan
1151 K St. NW.
Washington, DC 20005
Aviation executive, author,
lecturer

Chesebrough-Ponds, Inc.
Nyala Farm Rd.
Westport, CT 06881-0851
Ralph E. Ward,
chairman of the board and CEO

Chevron Corp.
225 Bush St.
San Francisco, CA 94104
George M. Keller,
chairman of the board

Chicago
c/o Howard Kaufman, Frontline
Management
80 Universal City Plaza
Universal City, CA 91608
Pop-rock group

Child, Julia McWilliams
c/o WGBH
125 Western Ave.
Boston, MA 02134
Author, television performer,
cooking expert

Chinh, Truong
Office of the President
Hanoi, Vietnam
President of Vietnam

Chiu, Yam Tsi
2350 E. El Segundo Blvd.
El Segundo, CA 90245
Space physicist

Christie, Julie
One Selwood Terrace
London SW3 England
Actress

Christopher, Dennis
151 El Camino Dr.
Beverly Hills, CA 90212
Actor

Chrysler Corp.
12000 Lynn Townsend Dr.
Detroit, MI 48288
*Lee A. Iacocca,
chairman of the board and CEO*

**Chung, Connie
(Constance Yu-Hwa
Chung)**
c/o NBC
30 Rockefeller plaza
New York, NY 10112
Broadcast journalist

The Church Lady
c/o NBC-TV
30 Rockefeller Plaza
New York, NY 10112
Hostess for Church Chat

**Church of Monday Night
Football**
P.O. Box 2127
Santa Barbara, CA 93120
Reverend Rick Slade

**Church's Fried Chicken,
Inc.**
355 Spencer Ln.
San Antonio, TX 78284
*J. David Bamberger,
chairman of the board and CEO*

Cigna Corp.
One Logan Sq.
Philadelphia, PA 19103
*Robert D. Kilpatrick,
chairman of the board and CEO*

Cimino, Michael
151 El Camino Dr.
Beverly Hills, CA 90212
Motion picture director

Cinderella
c/o Larry Mazer, Entertainment
Services
212 Race St.
Philadelphia, PA 19106
Heavy metal rock group

**Circle K Convenience
Stores**
4500 S. 40th St.
Phoenix, AZ 85040
*Karl Eller,
chairman of the board and CEO*

Circuit City Stores, Inc.
2040 Thalboro St.
Richmond, VA 23230
*Alan L. Wurtzel,
chairman of the board and CEO*

Citicorp
399 Park Ave.
New York, NY 10022
*John S. Reed,
chairman of the board*

THE ADDRESS BOOK

The Civil War Round Table of New York
P.O. Box 3485
New York, NY 10185
*Roy B. Greenfield, president.
Experts in the field of the Civil War*

Claiborne, Liz
(Liz Claiborne Ortenberg)
1441 Broadway
New York, NY 10018
Women's clothing designer

Clapton, Eric
1888 Century Park E., Suite 1400
Los Angeles, CA 90067
Rock guitarist, singer, songwriter

Clare, Stewart
NW. Woodland Rd.
Indian Hills in Riverside
Kansas City, MO 64150
Research biologist, educator

Clarey, Donald Alexander
White House
1600 Pennsylvania Ave.
Washington, DC 20500
Special assistant to the president

Clark, Dick
3003 W. Olive Ave.
Burbank, CA 91505
Producer, Entertainer

Clark, John Elwood
Mayor's Office
1220 SW. 5th Ave.
Portland, OR 97204
Mayor of Portland

Clark, John Whitcomb
1753 W. Congress Parkway
Chicago, IL 60612
Diagnostic radiologist

Clark, Peggy
23 Albatross St.
Woods Hole, MA 02543
Theatrical lighting designer

Clark, Roy
c/o Jim Halsey Co., Inc.
3225 S. Norwood Ave.
Tulsa, OK 74135
Singer, musician, business exec.

Clarke, Arthur Charles
25 Barnes Pl.
Colombo, Sri Lanka 7, India
Author

Clarke, Bobby
(Robert Earle Clarke)
c/o Philadelphia Flyers
Pattison Place
Philadelphia, PA 19148
Hockey player

Clarke, Kenneth Stevens
1750 E. Boulder St.
Colorado Springs, CO 80909
Special projects administrator

Clarke, Stanley Marvin
151 El Camino Dr.
Beverly Hills, CA 90272
Musician, composer

Claus, Santa
The North Pole
*Delivers gifts to good boys and
girls on Christmas*

Clayburgh, Jill
1888 Century Park E., Suite 1400
Los Angeles, CA 90067
Actress

Cleary, Beverly Atlee
c/o William Morrow
105 Madison Ave.
New York, NY 10016
Author

Clements, Vassar Carlton
P.O. Box 170
Hermitage, TN 37076
Fiddle player

Cleveland, James (Rev.)
P.O. Box 4632
Detroit, MI 48243
Gospel singer, composer, minister

Cleveland, Paul Mathews
US Ambassador to N.Z.
State Department
Washington, DC 20520
Ambassador to New Zealand

Clinton, William J.
State Capitol
Little Rock, AR 72201
Governor of Arkansas, lawyer

Clorox Co.
1221 Broadway
Oakland, CA 94612
*C. R. Weaver,
chairman of the board and CEO*

Close, Glenn
1888 Century Park E., Suite 1400
Los Angeles, CA 90067
Actress

Club Med, Inc.
40 W. 57th St.
New York, NY 10019
Serge Trigano, president

Club Nouveau
c/o King Jay
414 12th St.
Sacramento, CA 95814
Pop music group

Coburn, James
8899 Beverly Blvd.
Los Angeles, CA 90048
Actor

Coca-Cola Co.
310 North Ave. NW.
Atlanta, GA 30313
*Roberto C. Goizueta,
chairman of the board and CEO*

Coco, James
c/o Paul H. Wolowitz
59 E. 54th St.
New York, NY 10022
Actor

Cody, Iron Eyes
999 N. Doheny Dr. W., Suite 102
Los Angeles, CA 90069
Actor

Coggan, Frederick Donald
Kingshead House
Sissinghurst, Kent, England
Former archbishop of Canterbury

**Cohen, Leonard
(Norman Cohen)**
c/o Columbia Records
1801 Century Park W.
Century City, CA 90067
*Poet, novelist, musician,
songwriter*

Cohen, Michael S.
19701 S. Miles Road
Cleveland, OH 44128
Publisher, The Bathroom Journal,
*a general interest magazine de-
signed to be read in the bathroom*

Cohn, Alvin Gilbert
c/o Concord Jazz, Inc.
P.O. Box 845
Concord, CA 94522
Musician, jazz composer

Cohn, Sam
c/o International Creative
Management
40 W. 57th St.
New York, NY 10019
*Motion picture and theatrical
agent*

Colaianni, Jim
P.O. Box 3102
Margate, NJ 08437
Publisher of Sunday Sermon, *a
weekly publication of complete
homilies for use by the clergy*

Cole, Natalie Maria
c/o Dan Cleary Management
720 Holmby Ave.
Los Angeles, CA 90024
Singer

Coleman, Dabney W.
8899 Beverly Blvd.
Los Angeles, CA 90048
Actor

Coleman, Peter Tali
Office of the Governor
Pago Pago Tutuila
American Samoa 96799
Governor of American Samoa

Coleman, Vince
200 Stadium Plaza
St. Louis, MO 63102
Baseball player

Colgate-Palmolive Co.
300 Park Ave.
New York, NY 10022
Keith Crane,
chairman of the board

Colicos, John
9200 Sunset Blvd., Suite 625
Los Angeles, CA 90069
Actor

Collins, Joan Henrietta
10000 Santa Monica Blvd.
Suite 400
Los Angeles, CA 90067
Actress

Collins, Judy Marjorie
P.O. Box 1296, Cathedral Station
New York, NY 10025
Singer

Collins, Martha Layne
Office of Governor
State Capitol
Frankfort, KY 40601
Governor of Kentucky

Collins, Phil
c/o Atlantic Recording Group
75 Rockefeller Plaza
New York, NY 10019
Singer, songwriter, drummer,
record producer

Collins, Stephen
Box 95
Fitchville, CT 06334
Actor

Color Tile, Inc.
515 Houston St.
Fort Worth, TX 76102
John A. Wilson, chairman of the
board, president, CEO

Colson, Charles
P.O. Box 40562
Washington, DC 20016
Former member of Nixon
administration, convicted in Wa-
tergate trial

Comaneci, Nadia
Gherge Gheorghin-DEJ
Romania
Gymnast

The Commodores
39 W. 55th St.
New York, NY 10019
Soul group

Communications Satellite
Corp. (COMSAT)
950 L'Enfant Plaza, SW.
Washington, DC 20024
Irving Goldstein, chairman of the
board and CEO. Makers of the
first communications satellite

Como, Perry
RCA Records
1133 Ave. of the Americas
New York, NY 10036
Singer

Compton, Ann Woodruff
ABC News
1717 DeSales St. NW.
Washington, DC 20036
News correspondent

ComputerLand Corp.
30985 Santana St.
Hayward, CA 94544
Edward E. Faber,
chairman of the board

Concannon, Gary
2990 Redhill Ave.
Costa Mesa, CA 92626
President, Concannon's Horseless
Stable. Company will pick up and
clean, repair or restore your
Rolls-Royce

Concepcion, David Ismael
c/o Cincinnati Reds
100 Riverfront Stadium
Cincinnati, OH 45202
Baseball player

Condon, Richard
c/o Abner Stein
10 Roland Gardens
London SW 7 3ph England
Author

Connery, Sean
1888 Century Park E., Suite 1400
Los Angeles, CA 90067
Actor

Conniff, Ray
c/o CBS Records, Inc.
51 W. 52nd St.
New York, NY 10019
Conductor, composer

Connors, Chuck Kevin Joseph
4932 Lankershim Blvd., Suite 201
North Hollywood, CA 91601
Actor

Connors, James Scott (Jimmy Connors)
c/o Pro Serve, Inc.
888 17th St. NW.
Washington, DC 20006
Tennis Player

Connors, Mike (Krekor Ohanian)
c/o Charter Management
9000 Sunset Blvd.
Los Angeles, CA 90048
Actor

Conoco, Inc.
1007 Market St.
Wilmington, DE 19898
Ralph E. Bailey,
chairman of the board and CEO

Conrad, Charles, Jr.
3855 Lakewood Blvd.
Long Beach, CA 90846
Former astronaut, business exec.

**Conrad, Robert
(Conrad Robert Falk)**
15301 Ventura Blvd., Suite 345
Sherman Oaks, CA 91403
Actor

Conrad, William
15301 Ventura Blvd., Suite 345
Sherman Oaks, CA 91403
Actor, producer, director

Conti, Thomas Antonio
c/o Chatto and Linnit Globe
Theatre
Shaftesbury Ave.
London WI England
Actor

Convy, Bert
c/o International Creative
Management
8899 Beverly Blvd.
Los Angeles, CA 90048
Actor

Conway, Tim
c/o Phillip Weltman
425 S. Beverly Dr.
Beverly Hills, CA 90212
Comedian

Cooder, Ry
c/o Warner Brothers Records
Press Relations
3300 Warner Blvd.
Burbank, CA 91510
Guitarist, recording artist

Cook, Jeffrey Alan
1839 Senic Road
Fort Payne, AL 35967
Country musician

Cooke, Alfred Alistair
1150 5th Ave.
New York, NY 10128
Broadcaster, journalist

Cooksey, Frank
City Hall
P.O. Box 1088
Austin, TX 78767
Mayor of Austin, Texas

Coolidge, Rita
11684 Ventura Blvd., Suite 858
Studio City, CA 91604
Singer

Cooper, Jackie
1888 Century Park E., Suite 1400
Los Angeles, CA 90067
Actor

Coors, Jeffrey H.
East of Town
Golden, CO 80401
President, Adolph Coors Co.

Copland, Aaron
c/o Boosey & Hawkes, Inc.
24 W. 57th St.
New York, NY 10019
Composer

Coppola, Francis Ford
c/o Zoetrope Studios
916 Kearny St.
San Francisco, CA 94133
*Motion picture writer, producer,
director*

**Cord, Alex
(Alexander Viespi)**
c/o SGA Representation, Inc.
12750 Ventura Blvd., Suite 102
Studio City, CA 91604
Actor

Cordero, Angel T., Jr.
555 5th Ave., Room 1501
New York, NY 10019
Jockey

**Corea, Chick
(Armando Corea)**
2635 Griffith Park Blvd.
Los Angeles, CA 90039
Keyboardist, composer

Corman, Roger
c/o New Horizons Production
Co.
11600 San Vicente Blvd.
Los Angeles, CA 90049
Motion picture producer, director

Cornelius, Helen Lorene
P.O. Box 12321
Nashville, TN 37212
*Country music singer and
songwriter*

Corning Glass Works
Houghton Park
Corning, NY 14831
*James R. Houghton,
chairman of the board*

Corr, Edwin Gharst
El Salvadorean Embassy,
c/o Dept. of State
2201 C St.
Washington, DC 20520
*U.S. ambassador to El Salvador,
San Salvador*

Corrales, Patrick
c/o Cleveland Indians
Boudreau Blvd.
Cleveland, OH 44114
Baseball player, manager

Corwin, Norman
1840 Fairburn Ave.
Los Angeles, CA 90025
Writer, director, producer

Cosby, Bill
9255 Sunset Blvd., Suite 706
Los Angeles, CA 90069
*Comedian, actor, writer, director,
producer*

**Cosell, Howard
(Howard William Cohen)**
c/o New York Daily News
220 E. 42nd St.
New York, NY 10017
Sports journalist

**Costello, Elvis
(Declan Patrick McManus)**
c/o International Creative
Management
40 W. 57th St.
New York, NY 10019
Musician, songwriter

Cotlow, Lewis Nathaniel
132 Lakeshore Dr.
N. Palm Beach, CA 33408
Explorer

Cotten, Joseph
6363 Wilshire Blvd.
Los Angeles, CA 90048
Actor

Cousteau, Jaques Yves
c/o Couteau Society
777 3rd Ave.
New York, NY 10017
Marine explorer, film producer

Cousy, Bob Joseph
c/o Boston Celtics Press Relations
Boston Garden, North Station
Boston, MA 02114
*Sports commentator, former
basketball player*

Coyte, Kenneth A.
1995 Broadway
New York, NY 10023
*President, Worldwide Television
News, one of the world's leading
news services for bizarre stories*

**Craddock, Billy Wayne
(Crash Craddock)**
P.O. Box 6798
Greensboro, NC 27405
Entertainer

Crane, Irving Donald
270 Yarmouth Rd.
Rochester, NY 14610
Pocket billiards player

Cranston, Alan
112 Hart Office Bldg.
Washington, DC 20510
U.S. senator

Crawford, Broderick
132 Lasky Dr.
Beverly Hills, CA 90212
Actor

Crawford, J. P.
3501 County Road 20
Stanley, NY 14561
Educational materials specialist

Craxi, Bettino
Via Foppo 5
1-20144 Milan, Italy
Premier of Italy

Cray, Robert
c/o Mike Kappus, The Rosebud
Agency
P.O. Box 210103
San Francisco, CA 94121
Blues guitarist, singer, songwriter

Crenna, Richard
1888 Century Park E., Suite 1400
Los Angeles, CA 90067
Actor

Crenshaw, Ben
c/o U.S. Golf Association
Liberty Corners Rd.
Far Hills, NJ 07931
Golfer

Crichton, John Michael
9348 Santa Monica Blvd.
Beverly Hills, CA 90210
Author, motion picture director

**Crist, Judith
(Klein Crist)**
180 Riverside Dr.
New York, NY 10024
Film, drama critic

Crocker National Bank
One Montgomery St.
San Francisco, CA 94104
*Frank V. Cahouet,
chairman of the board and CEO*

Cronkite, Walter
c/o CBS News
524 W. 57th St.
New York, NY 10019
*Radio and television news
correspondent*

**Crosby, Kathryn
Grandstaff (Grant Crosby)**
c/o Station KPIX

855 Battery St.
San Francisco, CA 94111
Actress

Crosby, Norm
P.O. Box 48779
Los Angeles, CA 90048
Comedian

Cross, Christopher
114 W. 7th St., Suite 717
Austin, TX 78701
Recording artist

Croteau, Gary
8380 E. Hinsdale Ave.
Englewood, CO 80112
Hockey player

Crouch, Andrae
5525 Oakdale, Suite 110
Woodland Hills, CA 91364
Singer, composer, musician

Crowded House
c/o Gary Stamler
1900 Ave. of the Stars
Suite 1780
Los Angeles, CA 90067
Pop music group

Crown Books Corp.
500, 5th Ave.
Landover, MD 20785
Robert M. Haft, president

Cruise, Tom
1888 Century Park E., Suite 1400
Los Angeles, CA 90067
Actor

Cruz, Jose
New York Yankees
Yankee Stadium
Bronx, NY 10451
Baseball player

Crystal, Billy
8899 Beverly Blvd.
Los Angeles, CA 90048
Actor, comedian

Culp, Robert
10351 Santa Monica Blvd.
2nd Floor
Los Angeles, CA 90025
Actor, writer, director

The Cult
c/o International Creative
Management
40 W. 57th St.
New York, NY 10019
Hard rock group

Cunningham, Billy
CBS Sports
51 W. 52nd St.
New York, NY 10019
Television sportscaster

Cuomo, Mario Mathew
Office of Governor
State Capitol
Albany, NY 12224
Governor of New York

Curb, Michael Charles
3907 W. Alameda, 2nd Floor
Burbank, CA 91505
*Former lieutenant governor of
California, record company exec.*

The Cure
c/o International Talent Group
200 W. 57th St., Suite 1403
New York, NY 10019
Pop music group

Curtin, Jane Therese
1888 Century Park E., Suite 1400
Los Angeles, CA 90067
Actress, writer

**Curtis, Tony
(Bernard Schwartz)**
c/o Kurt Frings Associates
9440 Santa Monica Blvd.
Beverly Hills, CA 90212
Actor

Customs Last Stand
9023 Norma Place
West Hollywood, CA 90069
*Custom personal video
presentations, operated by Mary
Hart, Deidre Hall, and Cheri Ingram*

Cutler, Walter Leon
c/o NEA/ARP
Department of State
Washington, DC 20520
U.S. ambassador to Saudi Arabia

Dad's Root Beer Co.
600 S. Federal St.
Chicago, IL 60605
Roy Gurvey, president

Dabl, Arlene
c/o Charter Management
9000 Sunset Blvd.
Los Angeles, CA 90069
*Actress, beauty columnist, author,
fashion designer*

Dahl, Roald
Gypsy House
Great Missenden
Buckinghamshire, England
Writer

Dailey, Janet
Star Route 4
Box 2197
Branson, MO 65616
Romance novelist

Dairy Fresh Corp.
907 Tuscaloosa St.
Greensboro, AL 36744
*J. L. Morrison,
chairman of the board*

Dale, Jim
c/o Harold Schiff Gottlieb Schiff

555 5th Ave.
New York, NY 10017
Actor

Dali, Salvadore
Port Lligat
Cadaques, Spain
Artist

Daltry, Roger
c/o Left Services
157 W. 57th St.
New York, NY 10019
Rock singer

Daly, Tyne
409 N. Camden Dr., Suite 202
Beverly Hills, CA 90210
Actress

Damone, Vic
9046 Sunset Blvd., Suite 208
Los Angeles, CA 90069
Actor

Danforth, John Claggett
Senate Office Bldg.
497 Russell
Washington, DC 20510
U.S. senator

Dangerfield, Rodney (Jack Roy)
c/o Endler Associates
3920 Sunny Oak Rd.
Sherman Oaks, CA 91403
Actor, comedian

Daniels, Charlie
210 25th Ave. N., Suite 500
Nashville, TN 37203
Musician, songwriter

Daniels, William David
10000 Santa Monica Blvd.
Suite 305
Los Angeles, CA 90067
Actor

Danner, Blythe Katharine
9000 Sunset Blvd., Suite 315
Los Angeles, CA 90069
Actress

Danson, Ted
c/o NBC TV
3000 W. Alameda Blvd.
Burbank, CA 91523
Actor

Dantley, Adrian
Salt Palace, Suite 206
100 SW. Temple
Salt Lake City, UT 84101
Basketball player

Danza, Tony
c/o FHL Company
14319 Hartsook St.
Sherman Oaks, CA 91423
Actor

D.A.R.E. (Drug Abuse Resistance Education)
c/o LAPD D.A.R.E. Program
150 N. Los Angeles St.,
Mail Stop 439
Los Angeles, CA 90012
Lt. Rodger Coombs

Data General Corp.
4400 Computer Dr.
Westboro, MA 01580
*Edson De Castro,
cofounder and president*

Dattillo, Peggy
c/o National Enquirer
168 N. LaPeer
Beverly Hills, CA 90211
Columnist

David, Hal
15 W. 53rd St.
New York, NY 10019
Lyricist

David & David
c/o Perry Watts-Russell,
MFC Management
1803 S. Robertson, Number 201
Los Angeles, CA 90035
Rock group

Davidson, John
c/o Creative Artists Agency
190 N. Canon Dr.
Beverly Hills, CA 90210
Entertainer

Davis, Arthur Horace
U.S. Embassy
Avenida Mariscal Lopez 1776
Asuncion, Paraguay
U.S. ambassador to Paraguay

Davis, Bette Ruth Elizabeth
c/o Gottlieb, Schiff, Ticktin and Schachter
555 5th Ave., Number 1900
New York, NY 10017
Actress

Davis, James Robert (Jim)
c/o United Feature Syndicate, Inc.
200 Park Ave.
New York, NY 10166
Cartoonist, creator of "Garfield"

Davis, John Gilmore
Nuclear Regulatory Commission
Washington, DC 20555
Director of Nuclear Material Safety and Safeguards

Davis, Mac
c/o International Creative Management
8899 Beverly Blvd.
Los Angeles, CA 90048
Singer, songwriter

Davis, Mitchell P.
2500 Wisconsin Ave., Suite 930
Washington, DC 20007
Editor, Broadcast Interview Source, a list of thousands of interview guests for the media

Davis, Sammy, Jr.
400 S. Beverly Dr., Suite 410
Beverly Hills, CA 90212
Entertainer

Davis, Walter
P.O. Box 1369
Phoenix, AZ 85001
Basketball player

Dawber, Pam
151 El Camino Dr.
Beverly Hills, CA 90212
Actress

Dawson, Mary Ann Weforth (Mimi Dawson)
1919 M St.
NW. Washington, DC 20005
Commissioner of the FCC

Dawson, Richard
c/o ABC Press Relations
1330 Ave. of the Americas
New York, NY 10019
Actor, game show host

Day, Doris
P.O. Box 223163
Carmel, CA 93921
Actress, singer

Day, Lee
385 Broad St.
Bloomfield, NJ 07003
The Celebrity Pet Groomer

Day, Stacet Biswas
U Calabar College
Medical Science Calabar
Nigeria, West Africa
Physician, author, educator

Days Inn of America, Inc.
2751 Buford Highwav
Atlanta, GA 30324
*Henry R. Silverman,
chairman of the board and CEO*

Days of Our lives Fan Club (A Touch of Days)
116 Boston Ave.
North Arlington, NJ 07032
Sally Ann Morris, president

Dead or Alive
10100 Santa Monica Blvd.
16th Floor
Los Angeles, CA 90067
Pop music group

Dean, Jimmy
1341 W. Mockingbird Ln.
Suite 1100E
Dallas, TX 75247
*Meat processing company exec.,
entertainer*

Dean, John Gunther
U.S. Embassy in India
c/o US State Department
Washington, DC 20520
U.S. ambassador to India

Dean, Morton Nissan
c/o CBS News
524 W. 57th St.
New York, NY 10019
News correspondent

De Bakey, Michael Ellis
Baylor College of Medicine
One Baylor Plaza
Houston, TX 77030
Cardiovascular surgeon

DeBarge, El
c/o Tony Jones Management
6255 Sunset Blvd.
Los Angeles, CA 90028
Singer, songwriter

DeCinces, Douglas Vernon (Doug)
c/o California Angels,
Anaheim Stadium
2000 State College Blvd.
Anabeim. CA 92806
Baseball player

Decker, Mary Teresa
2923 Flintlock St.
Eugene, OR 97401-4660
Olympic runner

De Concini, Dennis
328 Hart Senate Office Bldg.
Washington, DC 20510
U.S. senator

Dedina, Eldon
P.O. Box 1630
Montery, CA 93940
Cartoonist

Dee, Ruby
c/o The Artists Agency
10000 Santa Monica Blvd.
Los Angeles. CA 90067
Actress

Deep Purple
c/o Premier Talent Agency
3 E. 54th St.
New York, NY 10022
Heavy metal rock group

Deere & Co.
John Deere Rd.
Moline, IL 61265
*Robert A. Hanson,
chairman and CEO*

Dees, Rick
c/o KIIS-FM
6255 Sunset Blvd.
Los Angeles, CA 90028
Disc jockey

Def Leppard
80 Warwick Gardens
London W14 8PR England
Rock band

De Givenchy, Hubert James Marcel Taffin (Givenchy)
3 Ave. George V
75008 Paris, France
Fashion designer

De Havilland, Olivia Mary
BP 156
75764 Paris Cedex 16, France
Actress

De Johnette, Jack
c/o Warner Brothers Publicity
75 Rockefeller Plaza, 20th Floor
New York, NY 10019
Musician

De la Madrid Hurtado, Miguel
Office of President
Palacio Nacional
Mexico City, Mexico
President of Mexico

De La Renta, Oscar
555 7th Ave.
New York, NY 10018
Fashion designer

De Laurentis, Dino
c/o De Laurentis Entertainment Group
8670 Wilshire Blvd.
Beverly Hills, CA 90211
Motion picture producer

Dell'Olio, Louis
c/o Anne Klein & Co.
205 W. 39th St.
New York, NY 10018
Chief designer for Anne Klein

Delta Air Lines, Inc.
Hartsfield Atlanta International Airport
Atlanta, GA 30320
Ronald W. Allen, president

Del Taco, Inc.
345 Baker St.
Costa Mesa, CA 92626
Wayne W. Armstrong, president

De Luise, Dom
151 El Camino Dr.
Beverly Hills, CA 90212
Actor

DeMann, Freddy
9200 Sunset Blvd., Penthouse 15
Los Angeles, CA 90069
Manager

The Demento Society
P.O. Box 884
Culver City, CA 90203
Fans of the Dr. Demento Radio
Show

**Deneuve, Catherine
(Catherine Dorleac)**
c/o Ufland-Roth Productions
10201 W. Pico Blvd.
Los Angeles, CA 90035
Actress

De Niro, Robert
c/o Jay Julien
1501 Broadway
New York, NY 10036
Actor

Dennehy, Brian
c/o Smith-Freedman & Associates
123 N. San Vicente Blvd.
Beverly Hills, CA 90211
Actor

Dennis, Sandy
9229 Sunset Blvd., Suite 306
Los Angeles, CA 90069
Actress

Denny's Restaurants
16700 Valley View Ave.
La Mirada, CA 90638
*Vern O. Curtis,
president and CEO*

**Dent, Bucky
(Russell Earl Dent)**
P.O. Box 1111
Arlington, TX 76010
Baseball player

Denton, Harold Ray
Nuclear Regulatory Commission
Nuclear Reactor Regulation
7920 Norfolk Ave.
Bethesda, MD 20555
Director, NRC

**Denton, Jeremiah An-
drew, Jr.**
U.S. Senate
Washington, DC 20510
U.S. senator

Denver, Bob
Box 426
Pacific Palisades, CA 90272
Actor

**Denver, John (Henry
John Deutschendorf, Jr.)**
P.O. Box 1587
Aspen, CO 81612
Singer, songwriter

De Palma, Brian Russell
c/o Fetch Productions
25 5th Ave.
New York, NY 10003
Motion picture writer and director

Depaulis, Palmer Anthony
300 City-County Bldg.
Salt Lake City, UT 84111
Mayor of Salt Lake City, Utah

Dern, Bruce Macleish
1888 Century Park E., Suite 1400
Los Angeles, CA 90067
Actor

Des Barres, Pamela
3575 Cahuenga Blvd., Suite 470
Los Angeles, CA 90068
Author, actress, ex-leader of the GTOs, (Girls Together Outrageously), a notorious groupie club

Designer Donuts
6660 Sunset Blvd.
Los Angeles, CA 90028
Dennis Hoffman

Deukmejian, George
Office of Governor
State Capitol
Sacramento, CA 95814
Governor of California

Devane, William
c/o International Creative
Management
8899 Beverly Blvd.
Los Angeles, CA 90048
Actor

Devito, Danny Michael
1888 Century Park E., Suite 1400
Los Angeles, CA 90067
Actor

DeVries, Dr. William C.
c/o Humana Hospital-Audubon
One Audubon Plaza Dr.
Louisville, KY 40217
Artificial heart surgeon

Dewhurst, Colleen
STE Representation Ltd.
1776 Broadway
New York, NY 10019
Actress

Diamond, Neil
P.O. Box 3357
Hollywood, CA 90028
Singer, composer, entertainer

Diamond Walnut Growers, Inc.
1050 S. Diamond St.
Stockton, CA 95201
F. R. Light, president and CEO

Princess Diana
Kensington Palace
London W8 England
Princess of Wales

Dickerson, Eric Demetric
c/o Los Angeles Rams
2327 W. Lincoln Ave.
Anaheim, CA 92801
Football player

**Dickinson, Angie
(Angeline Brown)**
151 El Camino Dr.
Beverly Hills, CA 90212
Actress

**Dickson, Robert George
Brian**
Supreme Court of Canada
Ottawa, ON. KIA OJI
Canada
Chief Justice of Canada

Diebold, John
c/o The Diebold Group, Inc.
475 Park Ave. S.
New York, NY 10016
Business executive

Digital Equipment Corp.
146 Main St.
Maynard, MA 01754
*Kenneth H. Olsen,
cofounder and president*

Dikoff, Jody
1510 Andalusia
Venice, CA 90291
*President of Futrex, a patent
consulting and advisement company*

Diller, Phyllis
163 S. Rockingham
Los Angeles, CA 90049
Actress, comedienne

DiMaggio, Joe
2150 Beach St.
San Francisco, CA 94123
Former baseball player

Diprete, Edward D.
State House
Smith St.
Providence, RI 02903
Governor of Rhode Island

The Disney (Walt) Co.
500 S. Buena Vista St.
Burbank, CA 91521
M. D. Eisner, chairman and CEO

Divorce Anonymous
543 N. Fairfax
Los Angeles, CA 90036
Tasha Schaal

Dixon, Alan John
U.S. Senate
Washington, DC 20510
U.S. senator

Dixon, Willie James
c/o Cameron Organization, Inc.
822 Milgrove Ave.
Western Springs, IL 60558
Musician

Dobbs, Gregory Allan
ABC News
2460 W. 26th Ave.
Denver, CO 80211
Journalist

Dobrynin, Anatoliy F.
Soviet Embassy
1125 16th St.
Washington, DC 20036
Soviet ambassador to U.S.

Dobson, Kevin
151 El Camino Dr.
Beverly Hills, CA 90212
Actor

Dole, Elizabeth Hanford
400 7th St. SW.
Washington, DC 20590
Former secretary, U.S. Dept of Transportation

Dole, Robert J.
141 Hart Senate Office Building
Washington, DC 20510
U.S. senator

Dollar Rent-A-Car Systems, Inc.
6141 W. Century Blvd.
Los Angeles, CA 90045
Henry J. Caruso, president

**Domenici, Pete
(Vichi Domenici)**
Suite 434 Dirksen Senate Office Building

Washington, DC 20510
U.S. senator

Domingo, Placido
c/o Eric Semon Associates, Inc.
111 W. 57th St.
New York, NY 10019
Tenor

Dominos Pizza, Inc.
3001 Earhart Rd.
Ann Arbor, MI 48106-0997
Thomas S. Monaghan, president

Donahue, Phil
30 Rockefeller Plaza, Suite 827
New York, NY 10112
Television talk show host

**Donaldson, Sam
(Samuel Andrew
Donaldson)**
ABC News
1717 Desales St. NW.
Washington, DC 20036
Journalist

**Donaldson, Stephen
Reeder**
c/o Del Rey Ballantine
201 E. 50th St.
New York, NY 10022
Author

Dondino
1600 E. Desert Inn Rd., Suite 203
Las Vegas, NV 89109
Entertainer

Dorsett, Tony
(Anthony Drew Dorsett)
c/o Dallas Cowboys
6116 N. Central Expressway
Dallas, TX 75206
Football player

Dotson, Robert Charles
NBC News, 100 Colony Sq.
1175 Peachtree St., Suite 300
Atlanta, GA 30361
Television news correspondent

Doubleday, Nelson
c/o Doubleday & Co., Inc.
245 Park Ave.
New York, NY 10017
Publisher, baseball team exec.

The Doughboy
200 S. 6th St.
Minneapolis, MN 55402
Pillsbury Co. spokesboy

Douglas, Charles Francis
802 Texas Dr.
Tifton, GA 31794
Agronomist

Douglas, Kirk
c/o Bryna Co.
141 El Camino Dr.
Beverly Hills, CA 90212
Actor

Douglas, Michael Kirk
1888 Century Park E., Suite 1400
Los Angeles, CA 90067
Actor, film producer

Dow Chemical Co.
2030 Willard H. Dow Center
Midland, MI 48640
P. F. Oreffice, president and CEO

Downs, Hugh Malcolm
ABC News 20/20
1330 Ave. of the Americas
New York, NY 10019
Radio and television broadcaster

Doyle, Patrick John
1081 Burrard St.
Vancouver, BC., V6Z 1Y6
Canada
Otolaryngologist

Drapeau, Jean
City Hall
Montreal PQ
Canada
Mayor of Montreal, Canada

Dreyers Grand Ice Cream, Inc.
5929 College Ave.
Oakland, CA 94618
William F. Cronk III, president

Dreyfuss, Richard Stephan
2355 Benedict Canyon Dr.
Beverly Hills, CA 90210-1434
Actor

Dr Pepper Co.
P.O. Box 225086
Dallas, TX 75265
W. W. Clements,
chairman and CEO

Drug Emporium, Inc.
1035 Clubview Blvd.
Worthington, OH 43085
Philip I. Wilber,
chairman of the board, president

Dryer, Fred
8278 Sunset Blvd.
Los Angeles, CA 90046
Actor, former football player

Drysdale, Donald Scott
c/o Sportsvision
875 N. Michigan Ave.
Chicago, IL 60611
Sports broadcaster

Duff, Cloyd Edgar
Ponderocks Rd.
Livermore, CO 80536
Timpanist

Duffy, Patrick
c/o Writers & Artists Agency
11726 San Vicente Blvd.
Suite 300
Los Angeles, CA 90049
Actor

Duke, Charles
280 Lakeview
New Braunfels, TX 78130
Astronaut

Dullea, Keir
c/o Phil Gersh Agency, Inc.
232 N. Canon Dr.
Beverly Hills, CA 90210
Actor

Dunaway, Faye
1888 Century Park E., Suite 1400
Los Angeles, CA 90067
Actress

Dunkin Donuts, Inc.
Pacella Park Dr.
Randolph, MA 02368
Thomas R. Schwarz, president

Dunlop Tire Corp.
2661 Long Rd.
Grand Island, NY 14072
Randall L. Clark,
president and CEO

Dunn, Jack
3433-5 S. Campbell
Springfield, MO 65807
President, Debit One, The Mobile
Bookkeeping Service, a book-
keeping service that comes to
your office

Duper, Mark Super
c/o Miami Dolphins
3550 Biscayne
Miami, FL 33157
Football player

Du Pont, Pierre Samuel IV
Legislative Hall
Dover, DE 19901
Governor of Delaware

Du Pont Co.
1007 Market St.
Wilmington, DE 19809
Richard Edwin Heckert,
chairman of the board, CEO

Duran, Roberto
Box 157, Arena Colon
Panama City, Panama
Boxer

Duran Duran
c/o International Talent Group
200 W. 57th St., Suite 1403
New York, NY 10019
Pop music group

Durenberger, David
Ferdinand
154 Russell Senate Office Bldg.
Washington, DC 20510
U.S. senator

Durning, Charles
9255 Sunset Blvd., Suite 1A05
Los Angeles, CA 90069
Actor

Duvall, Robert
3226 Serra Dr.
Malibu, CA 90265
Actor

Duvall, Shelly
151 El Camino Dr.
Beverly Hills, CA 90212
Actress

Dylan, Bob
(Robert Allen
Zimmerman)
P.O. Box 264
Cooper Station
New York, NY 10003
Singer, songwriter

Eagleton, Thomas Francis
SD-197 Dirksen Senate Office
Bldg.
Washington, DC 20510
U.S. senator

Eakin, Thomas Capper
2729 Shelly Rd.
Shaker Heights, OH 44122
Sports promotion executive

Eardley, Richard Roy
Office of Mayor, City Hall
P.O. Box 500
Boise, ID 83702
Mayor of Boise, Idaho

Earl, Anthony Scully
State Capitol
P.O. Box 7863
Madison, WI 53707
Governor of Wisconsin

Earnhardt, Ralph (Dale)
Route 8 Box 463
Mooresville, NC 28115
Race car driver

Eastern Airlines, Inc.
Miami International Airport
Miami, FL 33148
Frank Borman,
chairman and CEO

Eastman Kodak Co.
343 State St.
Rochester, NY 14650
Colby H. Chandler, chairman and
CEO

Easton, Sheena
8899 Beverly Blvd.
Los Angeles, CA 90048
Pop singer

Eastwood, Clint
Carmel by the Sea, City Hall
P.O. Box CC
Carmel by the Sea, CA 93921
Actor, mayor of Carmel
by the Sea

Eat N Park Restaurants, Inc.
100 Park Manor Dr.
Pittsburgh, PA 15205
James S. Broadhurst,
president and CEO

Eberhart, Richard
5 Webster Terrace
Hanover, NH 03755
Poet

Ebert, Roger Joseph
401 N. Wabash Ave.
Chicago, IL 60611
Film critic

Eckert, Lloyd
28 Bonning Court
Spring Valley, NY 10977
President, Beegotten Creations, a
company that makes and sells
men's maternity clothes

Eckstine, Billy
(William Clarence
Eckstine)
c/o Redbeard Presents Ltd.
1061 E. Flamingo Rd., Number 7
Las Vegas, NV 89109
Singer

Eden, Barbara Jean
10000 Santa Monica Blvd.
Suite 305
Los Angeles, CA 90067
Actress

Edwards, Blake
1888 Century Park E., Suite 1400
Los Angeles, CA 90067
Motion picture director

Edwards, Douglas
CBS
51 W. 52nd St.
New York, NY 10019
Radio, television news reporter

Egghead, Inc.
14784 NE. 95th St.
Redmond, VA 98052
Victor D. Alhadeff, president.
Computer software retailers

Eggleton, Arthur C.
City Hall
Toronto, ON M5H 2N2
Canada
Mayor of Toronto

Ehrlichman, John Daniel
P.O. Box 5559
Santa Fe, NM 87502
Author, former assistant to
President Nixon

Eikenberry, Jill
P.O. Box 900
Beverly Hills, CA 90213
Actress

Eisenberg, Kenneth Sawyer
1700 K St.
Washington, DC 20006
Restoration expert

Elam, Jack
P.O. Box 5718
Santa Barbara, CA 93150
Actor

Elder, Robert Lee
1725 K St. NW., Suite 1201
Washington, DC 20006
Golfer

Eliott, Bently Thomas
White House
1600 Pennsylvania Ave.
Washington, DC 20500
Director of speechwriting for the
White House

Elite Model Management Corp.
150 E. 58th St.
New York, NY 10155
John Casablancas, president

Queen Elizabeth II (Elizabeth Alexandra Mary)
Buckingham Palace
London SW1 England
Her Majesty Queen Elizabeth II, queen of United Kingdom of Great Britain and Northern Ireland and her other realms, head of the commonwealth and defender of the faith

Queen Elizabeth
Clarence House
London SW1 England
The queen mother

Ellis, Albert
45 E. 65th St.
New York, NY 10021
Clinical psychologist, author, educator

Ellison, Harlan Jay
3484 Coy Dr.
Sherman Oaks, CA 91423
Author

Elway, John
5700 Logan St.
Denver, CO 80216
Football player

Emerson Radio Corp.
One Emerson Ln.
North Bergen, NJ 07047
William W. Lane, chairman

Enberg, Dick
c/o NBC Sports
30 Rockefeller Plaza
New York, NY 10020
Sportscaster

Encyclopedia Britannica, Inc.
310 S. Michigan Ave.
Chicago, IL 60604
Robert P. Gwinn, chairman and CEO

End Violence Against the Next Generation
977 Keeler Ave.
Berkeley, CA 94708
Adah Maurer, Ph.D.

Englebreght, Roy
405 Vista Grande
Newport Beach, CA 92660
Director and founder, Sportscaster Camps of America

English, Alexander
P.O. Box 4286
Denver, CO 80204
Basketball player

Eno, Brian
c/o Warner Brothers
Records, Inc.
3300 Warner Blvd.
Burbank, CA 91510
Composer, musician, producer

Enriquez, Rene
9200 Sunset Blvd., Suite 601
Los Angeles, CA 90069
Actor

Equitable Life Assurance
787 7th Ave.
New York, NY 10019
Robert F. Froehlke, chairman

Erman, John
2049 Century Park E., Suite 3700
Los Angeles, CA 90067
*Motion picture and television
director*

Erving, Julius Winfield
Veterans Stadium
P.O. Box 25040
Philadelphia, PA 19147
Basketball player

Eskimo Pie Corp.
530 E. Main St.
Richmond, VA 23219
*David P. Reynolds,
chairman and CEO*

Ethan Allen, Inc.
Ethan Allen Dr.
Danbury, CT 06810
*Nathan S. Ancell,
chairman and CEO*

Etheredge, Forest Deroyce
52 W. Downer St.
Aurora, IL 60506
U.S. senator

Eubanks, Bob
23801 Calabassas Rd.
Number 205045
Calabassas, CA 91302-4547
Television entertainer

Europe
P.O. Box 404
San Francisco, CA 94101
Rock group

Evans, Daniel Jackson
U.S. Senate
Washington, DC 20510
U.S. senator

Evans, Gil
c/o MCA Records
70 Universal City Plaza
Universal City, CA 91608
Musician, composer

Evans, John Victor
Statehouse, 2nd Floor
Boise, ID 83720
Governor of Idaho

Evans, Linda
c/o Charter Management
9000 Sunset Blvd.
Los Angeles, CA 90069
Actress

Evans, Robert
c/o Paramount Pictures Corp.
5555 Melrose Ave.
Los Angeles, CA 90038
Motion picture producer

Evans, Samuel London
IVB Building
1700 Market St., Suite 2020
Philadelphia, PA 19103
Impresario

Everly, Don
P.O. Box 2605
Nashville, TN 37219-0605
Singer, songwriter

Evers, John W.
10938 S. State St.
Chicago, IL 60628
Christian actor

Evert, Christine Marie (Chris)
c/o U.S. Tennis Association
51 E. 42nd St.
New York, NY 10017
Tennis player

Exile
510 W. Short
Lexington, KY 40507
Music group

Exon, John James
340 Dirksen Senate Office Bldg.
Washington, DC 20510
U.S. senator

Expose
c/o The Pantera Group
14352 SW. 142nd Ave.
Miami, FL 33186
Pop music group

Expose
P.O. Box 11191
Alexandria, VA 22313
Organization for the protection of rights of former spouses

Exxon Corp.
1251 Ave. of the Americas
New York, NY 10020-1198
C. C. Garvin, Jr., chairman and CEO

Fabius, Laurent
15 Palace du Panteon
Paris, France
Prime minister of France

**The Fabulous Thunder-
birds**
3001 Lake Austin Blvd.
Austin, TX 78703
Rock and blues band

King Fahd
Royal Palace
Riyadh, Saudi Arabia
King of Saudi Arabia

Failure Analysis Associates
2225 E. Bayshore Rd.
Palo Alto, CA 94303
Dr. Bernard Ross, chairman

**Fairbanks, Douglas Elton,
Jr.**
c/o Inverness Corp.
545 Madison Ave.
New York, NY 10022
*Actor, producer, writer, corpora-
tion director*

Fairchild, Morgan
9000 Sunset Blvd., 12th Floor
Los Angeles, CA 90069
Actress

Falk, Peter
1004 N. Roxbury Dr.
Beverly Hills, CA 90210
Actor

Falwell, Rev. Jerry
P.O. Box 1111
Lynchburg, VA 24505
*Television evangelist, head of the
Moral Majority*

Farentino, James
151 El Camino Dr.
Beverly Hills, CA 90212
Actor

Fargo, Donna
P.O. Box 15527
Nashville, TN 37215
*Country western singer,
songwriter*

Farley, Walter Lorimer
c/o Random House
201 E. 50th St.
New York, NY 10022
Author

Farmer, Philip Jose
c/o Berkely Publishing Group
200 Madison Ave.
New York, NY 10016
Author

Farmers Group, Inc.
4680 Wilshire Blvd.
Los Angeles, CA 90010
Richard G. Lindsley,
chairman and CEO

Farr, Jamie
P.O. Box 8519
Calabasas, CA 91302
Actor

Farrakhan, Louis
Nation of Islam
813 E. Broadway
Phoenix, AZ 85001
Political extremist

Farrell, Mike
Box 5061-306
Sherman Oaks, CA 91413
Actor

Farrow, Mia Villiers
c/o Lionel Larner Ltd.
850 7th Ave.
New York, NY 10019
Actress

Far West Savings & Loan Association
4001 MacArthur Blvd.
Newport Beach, CA 92660
William Belzberg, chairman

Fasi, Francis F.
Mayor's Office
City Hall
Honolulu, HI 96813
Mayor of Honolulu

The Fat Boys
c/o Tin Pan Apple, Inc.
250 W. 57th St., Room 1723
New York, NY 10107
Rap group

Fawcett, Farrah Leni
151 El Camino Dr.
Beverly Hills, CA 90212
Actress

F B F Nuclear Containers
1201 Hilton Rd.
Knoxville, TN 37921
Hezz Stringfield, Jr., president.
Manufactures storage containers
for nuclear wastes

Federal Express Corp.
2990 Airway
Memphis, TN 38194
Fredrick W. Smith,
chairman, president, and CEO

Federated Group, Inc.
5655 Union Pacific Ave.
Los Angeles, CA 90022
Wilfred Schwartz,
chairman and CEO

Feiffer, Jules
c/o Universal Press Syndicate
4400 Johnson Dr.
Fairway, KS 66205
Cartoonist, writer

Feinstein, Diane
Office of the Mayor
City Hall
San Francisco, CA 94102
Mayor of San Francisco

Feldon, Barbara
1888 Century Park E., Suite 1400
Los Angeles, CA 90067
Actress

Feliciano, Jose
c/o International Music
Management
6525 W. Sunset Blvd.
Hollywood, CA 90028
Entertainer

Fellini, Federico
10 Via Margutta
Rome, Italy
*Motion picture writer and
director*

Females For Felons
51 E. 42nd St., Number 517
New York, NY 10017
Ralph Sturges, coordinator

Ferch, John A.
U.S. Ambassador to Honduras
American Embassy
APO Miami, FL 34022
U.S. ambassador to Honduras

Ferguson, Maynard
P.O. Box 716
Ojai, CA 93023
Trumpet player

Ferm, Vergil Harkness
Dogford Rd.
Etna, NH 03750
Embryologist

Ferraro, Geraldine Anne
108-18 Queens Blvd.
Forest Hills, NY 11375
*Lawyer, first woman
vice-presidential candidate*

Ferrer, Jose Vicente
P.O. Box 616
Coconut Grove, FL 33133
Actor, producer, director

Ferrigno, Lou
621 17th St.
Santa Monica, CA 90402
Actor, bodybuilder

Ferry, Bryan
c/o Eg Management Inc.
161 W. 54th St.
New York, NY 10019
Singer, songwriter

Fiat U.S.A., Inc.
375 Park Ave.
New York, NY 10022
Francesco Gallo, chairman

Fidelity National Bank
440 Riverside Mall
Baton Rouge, LA 70821
*Donald F. Gerald,
chairman, CEO, and president*

Field, Sally
1888 Century Park E., Suite 1400
Los Angeles, CA 90067
Actress

**Filosa, Gary Fairmont
Randolph De Marco II**
P.O. Box 1315
Beverly Hills, CA 90213
Financier

**Fingers, Rollie
(Roland Glen Fingers)**
Milwaukee County Stadium
Milwaukee, WI 53214
Baseball player

Finney, Ross Lee
c/o University of Michigan School
of Music
Ann Arbor, MI 48109
Composer

**Firestone Tire & Rubber
Co.**
1200 Firestone Pky.
Akron, OH 44317
*John J. Nevin,
chairman, CEO, and president*

Fischer, Henry George
Rural Route One, Box 389
Sherman, CT 06784
Egyptologist

Fishel, Lesley Henry Jr.
1500 Buckland Ave.
Fremont, OH 43420
Historic site administrator

Fisher, Carrie
8966 Sunset Blvd.
Hollywood, CA 90069
Actress

Fisk, Carlton
c/o Comiskey Park
324 W. 35th St.
Chicago, IL 60616
Baseball player

Fitzgerald, Ella
c/o Norman Granz
451 N. Canon Dr.
Beverly Hills, CA 90210
Singer

Fitzgerald, Geraldine
655 Madison Ave.
New York, NY 10021
Actress

Fitzwater, Max Marlin
White House
1600 Pennsylvania Ave.
Washington, DC 20220
*Press secretary to the
vice president*

The Fixx
1776 Broadway, 6th Floor
New York, NY 10019
Pop music group

Flack, Roberta
c/o Atlantic Records
75 Rockefeller Plaza
New York, NY 10019
Singer

Flanagan, Fionnula Manon
c/o Abrams Harris & Goldberg Ltd.
9220 Sunset Blvd., Garden Suite B
Los Angeles, CA 90069
Actress

Flanagan, Michael Kendall
c/o Baltimore Orioles
Memorial Stadium
Baltimore, MD 21218
Baseball player

Flanders, Edward Paul
c/o Artists Agency
190 N. Canon Dr.
Beverly Hills, CA 90210
Actor

Flaum, Marshall Allen
301 S. Rodeo Dr.
Beverly Hills, CA 90212
Television producer, writer, and director

Fleetwood, Mick
c/o International Creative Management
40 W. 57th St.
New York, NY 10019
Musician, cofounder of Fleetwood Mac

Fleming, Peggy Gale
P.O. Box 173
Los Gatos, CA 95030
Figure skater

Fletcher, Louise
151 El Camino Dr.
Beverly Hills, CA 90212
Actress

Flock of Seagulls
526 Nicolett Mall
Minneapolis, MN 55402
Pop music group

Flowers, Wayland
7929 Hollywood Blvd.
Los Angeles, CA 90046
Entertainer

Fluor Corp.
3333 Michelson Dr.
Irvine, CA 92730
D. S. Tappan, Jr., chairman and CEO

Flynn, Frank Patrick
Earl Avenue at Wallace
Lafayette, IN 47902
Construction company exec.

Flynn, Raymond Leo
Boston City Hall
One City Hall Plaza
Boston, MA 02201
Mayor of Boston

Flynt, Larry Claxton
2029 Century Park E., Suite 3800
Los Angeles, CA 90067
Owner and publisher, Hustler and Chic magazines

Foch, Nina
P.O. Box 1884
Beverly Hills, CA 90213
Actress

**Fogelberg, Dan
(Daniel Grayling
Fogelberg)**
c/o Frontline Management
80 Universal City Plaza
Universal City, CA 91608
Recording artist

Fogerty, John
P.O. Box 9245
Berkeley, CA 94709
Rock singer, guitarist, songwriter

Folger Coffee Co.
One Procter & Gamble Plaza
Cincinnati, OH 45202
*John E. Pepper,
president and CEO*

Fonda, Jane
P.O. Box 491355
Los Angeles, CA 90049
Actress

Fonda, Peter
151 El Camino Dr.
Beverly Hills, CA 90212
Actor

Fontaine, Joan
P.O. Box 222600
Carmel, CA 93922
Actress

**Foodarama Supermarkets,
Inc.**
303 W. Main St.
Freehold, NJ 07728
*Joseph J. Saker,
chairman, president, and CEO*

Football Hall of Fame
Canton, OH 44708

Foote, Horton
c/o Dramatists Play Service, Inc.
440 Park Ave. S.
New York, NY 10016
Playwright, scriptwriter

Forbes, Malcolm Stevenson
60 5th Ave.
New York, NY 10011
*Publisher, author, former state
senator*

**Ford, Betty (Elizabeth)
Bloomer**
P.O. Box 927
Rancho Mirage, CA 92262
Wife of former U.S. president

**Ford, Ernest Jennings
(Tennessee Ernie)**
P.O. Box 31-552
San Francisco, CA 94131
Entertainer

Ford, Gerald Rudolph, Jr.
2100 Century Park W.
Los Angeles, CA 90067
Former president of the U.S.

**Ford, Glenn
(Gwyllyn Samuel Newton
Ford)**
15301 Ventura Blvd., Suite 345
Sherman Oaks, CA 91403
Actor

Ford, Harrison
P.O. Box 49344
Los Angeles, CA 90049-0344
Actor

Ford Motor Co.
American Rd.
Dearborn, MI 48121
*Donald E. Petersen,
chairman and CEO*

Ford, Wendell Hampton
U.S. Senate
Washington, DC 20510
U.S. senator

Forester Sisters Fan Club
128 Volunteer Dr.
Hendersonville, TN 37075
Fran Dalton, president

Forman, Milos
c/o Robert Lantz
888 7th Ave.
New York, NY 10106
Motion picture director

Forsythe, John
c/o Aaron Spelling
Productions, Inc.
132 S. Rodeo Dr.
Beverly Hills, CA 90212
Actor

**Fortune, Jimmy
(Lester James Fortune)**
P.O. Box 2703
Staunton, VA 24401
*Musician, member of the Statler
Brothers*

**Foster, Jodie
(Alicia Christian Foster)**
c/o International Creative
Management
8899 Beverly Blvd.
Los Angeles, CA 90048
Actress

Fotomat Corp.
205 9th St. N.
St. Petersburg, FL 33701
Shigeru Suzuki, president

Fountain, Pete
As Was 2
Poydras St.
New Orleans, LA 70140
Clarinetist

**Fourie, Bernardus
Gerhardus**
South African Embassy
3051 Massachusetts Ave.
NW. Washington, DC 20008
South African ambassador to U.S.

Fouts, Daniel Francis
P.O. Box 20666
San Diego, CA 92120
Football player

Fowles, John
c/o Jonathan Cape Ltd.
32 Bedford Sq.
London WC1B 3EL England
Author

Fox, James A.
220 Huntington Plaza
Northeastern University
Boston, MA 02115
Professor, expert in mass murder and serial murder

Fox, Samantha
1133 Ave. of the Americas
New York, NY 10036
Singer

**Foxx, Redd
(John Elroy Sanford)**
c/o ABC-TV
1330 Ave. of the Americas
New York, NY 10019
Actor, comedian

**Foyt, Anthony Joseph Jr.
(A.J.)**
6415 Toledo
Houston, TX 77008
Race car driver

Frady, Marshall Bolton
ABC News
7 W. 66th St.
New York, NY 10023
Television journalist, author

Frampton, Peter
565 5th Ave., Suite 600
New York, NY 10017
Musician, singer

Francis, Genie
15237C Magnolia Blvd.
Sherman Oaks, CA 91403
Actress

Franciscus, James Grover
8899 Beverly Blvd.
Los Angeles, CA 90048
Actor

Franck, Frederick Sigfred
Route 1, Box 165
Pacem In Terris
Covered Bridge Rd.
Warwick, NY 10990
Dental surgeon, artist, author

Frankenthaler, Helen
c/o Andre Emmerich
41 E. 57th St.
New York, NY 10022
Painter

Franklin, Aretha
8450 Linwood St.
Detroit, MI 48206
Singer

Franklin, Bonnie Gail
1888 Ave. of the Stars
Suite 1400
Los Angeles, CA 90067
Actress

Fraser, Donald Mackay
Office of Mayor
City Hall
Minneapolis, MN 55415
Mayor of Minneapolis

Frazetta, Frank
82 S. Courtland St.
East Stroudsburg, PA 18301
Artist

Frazier, Dallas June
Route 5, Box 149
Longhollow Pike
Gallatin, TN 37066
Singer, songwriter

Frazier, Joe
6290 Sunset Blvd., Suite 326
Los Angeles, CA 90028
Retired prize fighter

**Fredericks, Marshall
Maynard**
4113 N. Woodward Ave.
Royal Oak, MI 48053
Sculptor

Freedman, David Noel
P.O. Box 7344
Ann Arbor, MI 48107
Educator

**Freeman, Albert
Cornelius, Jr.**
c/o ABC Press Relations
1330 Ave. of the Americas
New York, NY 10019
Actor

Frey, Glenn
7250 Beverly Blvd., Suite 200
Los Angeles, CA 90036-2560
Singer, songwriter, guitarist

Friendly, Fred W.
Columbia University
Graduate School of Journalism
New York, NY 10027
Journalist, educator

**Friends of Veteran Soap
Actors**
P.O. Box 6039
Bluefield, WV 24701
Denise Clifton, president

Frome, Lynette
Reformatory for Women
Alderson, WV 24910
Convicted for assassination attempt against Gerald Ford

Frost, David
c/o David Paradine Ltd.
Breakfast TV Ctr.
Hawley Crescent
London NW1 England
Author, producer, columnist

Fuller, Samuel
c/o Chasen-Park-Citron
9255 Sunset Blvd.
Los Angeles, CA 90069
Motion picture writer and director, novelist

Fulton, Richard Harmon
Metropolitan Courthouse
Nashville, TN 37201
Mayor of Nashville

Furth, George
c/o Artists Agency
190 N. Canon Dr.
Beverly Hills, CA 90210
Actor, playwright

Gabor, Zsa Zsa
8721 Melrose Ave., Suite 108
Los Angeles, CA 90069
Actress

Gabriel, Charles Alvin
Joint Chiefs of Staff
The Pentagon
Washington, DC 20310
Chief of staff, U.S. Air Force

Gabriel, Peter
c/o International Talent Group
200 W. 57th St., Suite 1403
New York, NY 10019
Singer, songwriter, musician

**Gail, Max (Maxwell
Trowbridge Gail, Jr.)**
151 El Camino Dr.
Beverly Hills, CA 90212
Actor, director, musician

Gailey, Christine W.
220 Huntington Plaza
Northeastern University
Boston, MA 02115
Assistant professor, expert in violence and competition

Gainey, Robert Michael
c/o Montreal Canadiens
2313 Saint Catherine St.
W Montreal PQ H3H 1N2
Canada
Hockey player

Gajdusek, Daniel Carleton
National Institute of Health
Bethesda, MD 20205
Pediatrician, research virologist

Gallagher
P.O. Box 657
N. Hollywood, CA 91603
Comedian

Gallo, Ernest
600 Yosemite Blvd.
Modesto, CA 95354
Co-owner, E&J Gallo Winery

Gallo, Julio
E&J Gallo Winery
600 Yosemite Blvd.
Modesto, CA 95354
Co-owner, E&J Gallo Winery

Gallo, William
220 E. 42nd St.
New York, NY 10017
Cartoonist

Galloway, Don
c/o Beakle and Jennings
427 N. Canon Dr.
Beverly Hills, CA 90210
Flutist

Gallup, George Horace III
P.O. Box 628
Princeton, NJ 08540
Research organization exec.

Galway, James
c/o London Artists
73 Baker St.
London WIM IAH England
Flutist

**Gamblers Anonymous
Fellowship**
P.O. Box 17173
Los Angeles, CA 90017
Jim Z., national exec. secretary

Gandolf, Raymond
ABC News
7 W. 66th St.
New York, NY 10023
Media correspondent

Gannett Co., Inc.
P.O. Box 7858
Washington, DC 20044
*Alan H. Neuharth, chairman and
CEO. A media corporation, pub-
lishers of USA Today*

Gannon, John A.
1750 New York Ave. NW.
Washington, DC 20006
*President, International Associa-
tion of Fire Fighters*

The Gap, Inc.
900 Cherry Ave.
San Bruno, CA 94066
*Donald G. Fisher,
cofounder and president*

Garagiola, Joe
c/o FSM, Inc.
75 Rockefeller Plaza
Number 1100
New York, NY 10019
Radio and television personality

**Garcia, Jerry
(Jerome John Garcia)**
P.O. Box 1065
San Rafael, CA 94902
*Musician, guitarist for the
Grateful Dead*

Gardenia, Vincent
c/o Jay Julien
1501 Broadway
New York, NY 10036
Actor

Gardner, Ava
151 El Camino Dr.
Beverly Hills, CA 90212
Actress

Gardner, Booth
401 Pontius Ave. N.
Seattle, WA 98109
Governor of Washington

Gardner, Dale Allan
c/o Johnson Space Center
Houston, TX 77058
Astronaut, naval officer

Gardner, Russ
7850 Alabama Blvd.
Canoga Park, CA 91304
*Owner, Fiddler on the Roof,
a company specializing in
chimney sweeping*

Garfield, Brian Wynne
P.O. Box 376
Alpine, NJ 07620
Author

Garn, Edward Jacob
505 Dirksen Senate Office Bldg.
Washington, DC 20510
U.S. senator

Garr, Teri
8436 W. 3rd St., Number 650
Los Angeles, CA 90048
Actress

Garrett, Leif
9000 Sunset Blvd., Suite 1115
Los Angeles, CA 90069
Actor, pop singer

Garrett, Murray
20257 Prairie St.
Chatsworth, CA 91311
*President, Diener Industries, Inc.,
one of the largest manufacturers
of custom-designed erasers*

Garriot, Owen K.
c/o Johnson Space Center
Houston, TX 77058
Astronaut, scientist

Garvey, Steven Patrick
P.O. Box 2000
San Diego, CA 92120
Baseball player

Gastineau, Marcus D.
c/o New York Jets
598 Madison Ave.
New York, NY 10022
Football player

**Gately, George
(Gallagher Gately)**
McNaught Syndicate, Inc.
537 Steamboat Rd.
Greenwich, CT 06830
Cartoonist, creator of "Heathcliff"

Gautier, Dick
c/o Joss Rond
280 Santa Rosa Ln.
Montecito, CA 93108
Actor

Gavin, John
P.O. Box 961
Beverly Hills, CA 90213
Actor, business exec.,
former diplomat

Gay Community News
167 Tremont St.
Boston, MA 02111
Richard Burns

Gayle, Crystal
c/o Paul Shefrin
800 S. Robertson Blvd.
Los Angeles, CA 90038
Singer

Gaynor, Mitzi
9200 Sunset Blvd., Penthouse 7
Los Angeles, CA 90069
Entertainer

Gazzara, Ben
c/o J. Julien
1501 Broadway
New York, NY, 10036
Actor

Gebel-Williams, Gunther
Ringling Bros. Barnum & Bailey
Combined Shows, Inc.
320 New Mexico Ave.
NE. Washington, DC 20016
Animal trainer

Geffen, David
9130 Sunset Blvd.
Los Angeles, CA 90069
President, Geffen Records and
Geffen Film Co.

Geisel, Theodore Seuss
(Dr. Seuss)
7301 Encellia Dr.
La Jolla, CA 92037
Author, artist, television producer,
publisher

Geissler, Val
P.O. Box 1274
Hamilton, MT 59840
Singer

Gelbart, Larry
9255 Sunset Blvd., Suite 609
Los Angeles, CA 90069
Television producer, writer

Gemayel, Amin
Office of the President
Beirut, Lebanon
President of Lebanon

General Cinema Corp.
27 Boylston St.
Newton, MA 02167
Richard A. Smith, chairman

General Dynamics Corp.
Pierre Laclede Center
St. Louis, MO 63105
Stanley C. Pace,
chairman and CEO

General Electric Co.
3135 Easton Tpk.
Fairfield, CT 06430
John F. Welch, Jr.,
chairman and CEO

General Foods Corp.
250 North St.
White Plains, NY 10625
J. L. Ferguson, chairman and CEO

General Mills, Inc.
9200 Wayzata Blvd.
Minneapolis, MN 55440
*H. B. Atwater, Jr.,
chairman and CEO*

General Motors Corp.
3044 W. Grand Blvd.
Detroit, MI 48202
*Roger B. Smith,
chairman and CEO*

Genesis
c/o International Talent Group
200 W. 57th St., Suite 1403
New York, NY 10019
Pop music group

Genetics Institute, Inc.
87 Cambridge Park Dr.
Cambridge, MA 02140
G. Schmergel, president. Company performs biotechnology research, development, and production

Genuine Auto Parts Co.
2999 Circle 75 Pkwy.
Atlanta, GA 30339
*Wilton D. Looney,
chairman and CEO*

George, Phyllis
c/o Governor's Office
State Capitol
Frankfort, KY 40601
Sports broadcaster

George, Wally
P.O. Box 787
Hollywood, CA 90028
Arch-conservative television broadcaster

Georgia-Pacific Corp.
133 Peachtree St. NE.
Atlanta, GA 30303
*Dr. T. Marshall Hahn, Jr.,
chairman and CEO*

Georgia Satellites
c/o Praxis International
1700 Hayes St., Suite 301
Nashville, TN 37203
Rock and roll band

George, Lynda Day
291 S. La Cienega Blvd., Suite 307
Beverly Hills, CA 90211
Actress

Gephardt, Richard Andrew
218 Cannon House Office Bldg.
Washington, DC 20515
Congressman

Gerardia, Helen
490 West End Ave., Number 46
New York, NY 10024
Artist, educator

Gerber Products Co.
445 State St.
Fremont, MI 49412
*William S. McKinley,
chairman and CEO*

Gere, Richard
8436 W. 3rd St., Suite 650
Los Angeles, CA 90048
Actor

Gerulaitis, Vitas Kevin
c/o International Management
Group
One Erie View Plaza, Suite 1300
Cleveland, OH 44114
Tennis player

Gervin, George
P.O. Box 530
San Antonio, TX 78292
Basketball player

Getz, Stan
1560 Broadway, Number 507
New York, NY 10036
Saxophonist

Geyer, Frank
17922 Skypark Circle, Suite 6
Irvine, CA 92714
President of the Incredible Machine, a company that specializes in computer-engraved gifts

Ghiradelli Chocolate Co.
1111 139th Ave.

San Leandro, CA 94578
Dennis DeMomenico, CEO

Giant Food, Inc.
6300 Sheriff Rd.
Landover, MD 20785
*Israel Cohen,
chairman, president, and CEO*

Gibbs, June Nesbitt
163 Riverview Ave.
Middletown, RI 02840
U.S. senator

Gibbs, Marla (Margaret)
7060 Hollywood Blvd., Suite 206
Los Angeles, CA 90028
Actress

Gibson, Barry L.
821 N. Pine
Lansing, MI 48901
President, Celebrity Dirt. Collects and sells packages of dirt from stars' homes

Gibson, Debbie
c/o Broadbeard Productions, Inc.
29 Greene St.
New York, NY 10013
Pop singer, songwriter

Gibson, Mel
P.O. Box 72
Woollahra, 2025 New South
Wales
Australia
Actor

Gielgud, Sir Arthur John
c/o International Famous Agency
22 Grafton St.
London W1 England
Actor

Gifford, Frank Newton
ABC-TV
1330 Ave. of the Americas
New York, NY 10019
Broadcast journalist

Gillespie, Charles A., Jr.
U.S. Embassy to Colombia
State Dept.
Washington, DC 20520
U.S. ambassador to Colombia

Gillespie, Dizzy
(John Birks Gillespie)
1995 Broadway, Suite 501
New York, NY 10023
Musician

Gillette, Anita
c/o Smith Freedman & Associates
123 N. San Vicente Blvd.
Beverly Hills, CA 90211
Actress

The Gillette Co.
Prudential Tower Bldg.
Boston, MA 02199
*Colman M. Mockler, Jr.,
chairman and CEO*

Gilley, Mickey Leroy
4500 Spencer Highway
Pasadena, TX 77504
Musician

Gilliam, Terry Vance
c/o Doubleday & Co., Inc.
245 Park Ave.
New York, NY 10167
*Animator, film director, comedian
with Monty Python*

Gilmore, Artis
P.O. Box 530
San Antonio, TX 78292
Basketball player

Gimbel, Norman
P.O. Box 50013
Montecito, CA 93150
*Lyricist, music publisher,
television producer*

Ginsberg, Alan
c/o City Lights
261 Columbus Ave.
San Francisco, CA 94133
Poet

Ginzberg, Eli
845 West End Ave.
New York, NY 10025
*Economist, government consul-
tant, author*

Gish, Lillian
430 E. 57th St.
New York, NY 10022
Actress

Glass, Phillip
853 Broadway Room 2120
New York, NY 10003
Composer, musician

Glass, Ron
c/o Lawrence Kubik
9834 Wanda Park
Beverly Hills, CA 90210
Actor

Glenn, John Herschell, Jr.
503 Hart Office Bldg.
Washington, DC 20510
U.S. senator, former astronaut

Glenn, Scott
c/o Actor's Equity
165 W. 46th St.
New York, NY 10036
Actor

Gless, Sharon
1888 Century Park E., Suite 1400
Los Angeles, CA 90067
Actress

Glover, Danny
P.O. Box 885464
San Francisco, CA 94188
Actor

Godard, Jean Luc
7950 Sunset Blvd.
Los Angeles, CA 90046
Motion picture director

Golan, Menahem
6464 Sunset Blvd.
Hollywood, CA 90028
Chairman, the Cannon Group, Inc.

Goldberg, Gary David
c/o Paramount Pictures
555 Melrose Ave.
Hollywood, CA 90038
Writer, producer for TV's Family Ties

Goldberg, Leonard
c/o Paramount Pictures
555 Melrose Ave., DeMille Bldg., 2nd Floor
Los Angeles, CA 90038
Co-owner, Spelling-Goldberg Productions

Goldblum, Jeff
8500 Wilshire Blvd., Suite 801
Beverly Hills, CA 90211
Actor

Golden, William Theodore
40 Wall St.
New York, NY 10005
Corporate director and trustee

Goldsmith, Jerry
2049 Century Park E., Suite 3700
Los Angeles, CA 90067
Composer

Goldwater, Barry Morris
363 Russell Bldg.
Washington, DC 20510
U.S. senator

Goldwyn, Samuel John, Jr.
10203 Santa Monica Blvd.
Los Angeles, CA 90067
Motion picture producer

Good, Robert Alan
c/o Oklahoma Medical Research
Foundation
825 NE. 13th St.
Oklahoma City, OK 73104
Physician, educator

Gooden, Dwight
Shea Stadium
Roosevelt Ave. and 126th St.
Flushing, NY 11368
Baseball player

B. F. Goodrich Co.
500 S. Main St.
Akron, OH 44318
John D. Ong, chairman and CEO

Goodson, Mark
6340 Sunset Blvd.
Hollywood, CA 90028
Television producer

**Goodyear Tire & Rubber
Co.**
1144 E. Market St.
Akron, OH 44316
*Robert E. Mercer,
chairman and CEO*

Gorbachev, Mikhail
Office of the Chairman
Moscow, Soviet Union
*Chairman of Presidium of the
Soviet Union*

Gorcey, Elizabeth
9123 Sunset Blvd.
Los Angeles, CA 90069
Actress

Gore, Lesley
c/o Dick Fox Management
230 W. 55th St.
New York, NY 10019
Actress

Gorman, Cliff
1350 Ave. of the Americas
New York, NY 10019
Actor

Gorman, Greg
1351 Miller Dr.
Los Angeles, CA 90069
Photographer

Gorme, Eydie
P.O. Box 5140
Beverly Hills, CA 90210
Entertainer

Gorshin, Frank
P.O. Box 48559
Los Angeles, CA 90048
Actor

**Gossage, Goose
(Richard Michael Gossage)**
P.O. Box 200
San Diego, CA 92112
Baseball player

Gould, Elliot
8966 Sunset Blvd.
Hollywood, CA 90069
Actor

Gowdy, Curt
33 Franklin St.
Lawrence, MA 01840
Sportscaster

Graham, Bill
201 11th St.
San Francisco, CA 94103
Music producer

Graham, Billy
P.O. Box 779
Minneapolis, MN 55440
Evangelist

Graham, Bob (O. Robert Graham)
Office of the Governor
State Capitol
Tallahassee, FL 32301
Governor of Florida

Granatelli, Andy
24615 W. Park Miramar
Calabasas, CA 91302
Former race car driver, car tune-up chain owner

Grandy, Fred
151 El Camino Dr.
Beverly Hills, CA 90212
Actor

Granny Goose Foods, Inc.
930 98th Ave.
Oakland, CA 94603
Wesley Felton, president

Grant, Amy
P.O. Box 50701
Nashville, TN 37205
Contemporary gospel singer

Grant, James Pineo
c/o UNICEF
866 United Nations Plaza
New York, NY 10017
UNICEF official

Grateful Dead
c/o Grateful Dead Productions
P.O. Box 1073
San Rafael, CA 94915
Rock band

Grau, Shirley Ann
c/o Brandt & Brandt
1501 Broadway
New York, NY 10036
Writer

Graves, Peter
660 Channel Rd.
Santa Monica, CA 90402
Actor

Gray, Linda
P.O. Box 1370
Canyon Country, CA 91351
Actress

Great Western Financial Corp.
8484 Wilshire Blvd.
Beverly Hills, CA 90211
James F. Montgomery, chairman and CEO

Greenblatt, Milton
Neuropsychiatric Institute
760 Westwood Plaza
Los Angeles, CA 90024
Psychiatrist

Greene, Graham
c/o Bodley Head
9 Bow St.
London WC2 England
Author

Greene, Shecky
743 Uclan Dr.
Burbank, CA 91504
Entertainer

Greenstein, Judy
102 Orange Ave.
Long Beach, CA 90802
President, Cycle Express. Company offers services for the traveling business exec., including pet care

Greenwood, Lee
1204 17th Ave. S., Suite 300
Nashville, TN 37212
Country music recording artist

Gregory, James
8899 Beverly Blvd.
Los Angeles, CA 90048
Actor

Gretsky, Wayne
7424 118th Ave.
Edmonton, AB T56 4M9
Canada
Hockey player

Greyhound Corp.
Greyhound Tower
Phoenix, AZ 85013
*John W. Teets,
chairman and CEO*

Griese, Robert Allen
c/o Miami Dolphins
330 Biscayne Blvd.
Miami, FL 33132
Former football player

Griffin, Merv
1541 N. Vine St.
Hollywood, CA 90028
Entertainer, producer

Griffith, Andy
4445 Cartwright Ave. Suite 110
North Hollywood, CA 91602
Actor

Grimes, Tammy
10 E. 44th St. Suite 700
New York, NY 10017
Actress, singer

Grinzberg, Eli
845 West End Ave.
New York, NY 10025
Government consultant, economist, educator

Grodin, Charles
c/o The Ufland Agency
190 N. Canon Dr.
Beverly Hills, CA 90210
Actor, writer, director

THE ADDRESS BOOK

Grogan, Steven James
Schaffer Stadium
Route One
Foxboro, MA 02035
Football player

Grubbs, R. B.
625 W. Katella Ave., Suite 5
Orange, CA 92667
*President, Solmar Corp. Produces
and distributes bacteria that eat
waste products and control odors*

GTE Corp.
One Stamford Forum
Stamford, CT 06901
*Theodore F. Brophy,
chairman of the board*

Guard, Dave
1023 Mercedes Ave.
Los Altos, CA 94022
Musician

Guardino, Harry
c/o International Creative
Management
40 W. 57th St.
New York, NY 10019
Actor

Gucci, Aldo
8 Via Condotti
Rome, Italy 00187
Gucci stores executive

Gudonov, Alexander Boris
c/o Evelyn Shriver

341 West End Ave.
New York, NY 10023
Ballet dancer

Guerrero, Pedro
Dodger Stadium
1000 Elysian Park Ave.
Los Angeles, CA 90012
Baseball player

Guidry, Ron
Yankee Stadium
Bronx, NY 10451
Baseball player

**The Guiding Light Fan
Club**
2855 Stevens Ave.
Oceanside, NY 11572
Chris Mullen, president

Guillaume, Robert
1438 N. Gower Suite 31
Hollywood, CA 90028
Actor

Gulf Corp.
P.O. Box 1166
Pittsburgh, PA 15230
J. E. Lee, chairman and CEO

Gumbel, Bryant
c/o NBC
30 Rockefeller Plaza
New York, NY 10020
Cohost of The Today Show

Gurnsey, Robert
Box 1439
New London, NH 03257
President, National Survival Games. Company organizes and sells equipment for adult air-gun games

Guthrie, Arlo
The Farm
Washington, MA 01223
Folk singer

Guy, Thomas G.
11117 Mill Valley Rd.
Omaha, NE 68154
President, Merry Maids, Inc., one of the largest home cleaning companies in the U.S.

Habib, Philip Charles
1606 Courtland Rd.
Belmont, CA 94002
President's special envoy to Central America

Hackett, Buddy
151 El Camino Dr.
Beverly Hills, CA 90212
Comedian

Hackman, Gene
c/o Haldeman & Peckerman
9595 Wilshire Blvd., Suite 700
Beverly Hills, CA 90212
Actor

**Haden, Pat
(Pattrick Capper Haden)**
c/o CBS Sports
51 W. 52nd St.
New York, NY 10019
Former football player, sports commentator

Haenlein, George Friedrich Wilhelm
2071 S. College Ave.
Newark, DE 19702
Dairy scientist, educator

Hagar, Sammy
c/o E.L. Management
10100 Santa Monica Blvd.
Suite 2340
Los Angeles, CA 90067
Rock guitarist, songwriter, vocalist for Van Halen

Haggard, Merle Ronald
c/o HAG, Inc.
P.O. Box 536
Palo Cedro, CA 96073
Singer, songwriter, recording artist

Haggerty, Dan
10733 Arminta St.
Sun Valley, CA 91352
Actor

Hagler, Marvelous Marvin
c/o Marvelous Enterprises
28 Ward St.
Brockton, MA 02401
Boxer

Hagman, Larry
c/o Lorimar Productions
10202 W. Washington Blvd.
Culver City, CA 90232
Actor

Haig, Alexander Meigs, Jr.
1155 15th St. Suite 800
NW. Washington, DC 20005
*Former secretary of state,
1988 presidential candidate*

Hailey, Arthur
Lyford Cay
P.O. Box N-7776
Nassau, Bahamas
Author

Halberstam, David
c/o William Morrow & Co. Inc.
105 Madison Ave.
New York, NY 10016
Journalist, author

Haldeman, Joe William
5412 NW. 14th Ave.
Gainesville, FL 32605
Novelist

Hale, Clara
Hale House
154 W. 122nd St.
New York, NY 10027
Social activist

Haley, Alex Palmer
P.O. Box 3338
Beverly Hills, CA 90212
Author, foundation exec.

Haley, Jack (John J. Haley, Jr.)
8489 W. 3rd St.
Los Angeles, CA 90048
Director, producer, writer, exec.

Hall, Daryl
1888 Century Park E., Suite 1400
Los Angeles, CA 90067
Musician, singer, songwriter

Hall, Diedre
c/o NBC
3000 W. Alameda Ave.
Burbank, CA 91505
Actress

Hall, Donald Joyce
P.O. Box 580
Kansas City, MO 64141
Greeting card company exec.

Hall, Monty
2800 Olympic Blvd.
Santa Monica, CA 90404
Actor, television producer

Hall, Tom T.
P.O. Box 121089
Nashville, TN 37212
Songwriter, performer

Hallmark Cards, Inc.
2501 McGee Trafficway, Box 580
Kansas City, MO 64141
Donald J. Hall, chairman and CEO

Halston (Roy Halston Frowick)
c/o Halston Enterprises
645 5th Ave.
New York, NY 10022
Fashion designer

The Hamburglar
One McDonald Plaza
Oak Brook, IL 60521
Arch-thief of McDonaldland

Hamel, Veronica
9000 Sunset Blvd., Suite 1200
Los Angeles, CA 90069
Actress

Hamill, Dorothy Stuart
c/o International Management
Group
One Erieview Plaza
Cleveland, OH 44114
Figure skater

Hamill, Mark
c/o William Morris Agency
1350 Ave. of the Americas
New York, NY 10019
Actor

Hamilton, George
9000 Sunset Blvd., Suite 1200
Los Angeles, CA 90069
Actor

Hamilton Beach Co.
99 Scoville St.
Waterbury, CT 06706
John J. Flaherty, president

Hamlisch, Marvin
c/o Songwriter's Guild
276 5th Ave.
New York, NY 10001
Composer

Hammer, Armand
10889 Wilshire Blvd., Suite 1500
Los Angeles, CA 90024
*President, Occidental Petroleum,
patron of the arts*

Hammond, Jay Sterner
Capitol Building
Juneau, AK 99801
Governor of Alaska

Hamp, Eric Pratt
5200 S. Greenwood Ave.
Chicago, IL 60615
Linguist

Hampton, Daniel Oliver
55 E. Jackson, Suite 1200
Chicago, IL 60604
Football player

**Hancock, Herbie
(Herbert Jeffrey Hancock)**
1888 Century Park E., Suite 1400
Los Angeles, CA 90067
Composer, pianist, publisher

Hanna, William Denby
c/o Hanna-Barbera Productions
3400 W. Cahuenga Blvd.
Hollywood, CA 90068
*Cartoonist, cofounder of Hanna-
Barbera Productions*

Hanna-Barbera Productions, Inc.
3400 W. Cahuenga Blvd.
Hollywood, CA 90068
Charles S. Mechem, Jr., chairman

Hansen, Barret
c/o Imaginary Entertainment
925 Westmount Ave.
Los Angeles, CA 90043
aka "Dr. Demento," radio person-
ality

Harkin, Thomas R.
Hart Senate Office Bldg., Rm. 317
Washington, DC 20510
U.S. senator

The Harlem Globetrotters
15301 Ventura Blvd., Suite 430
Sherman Oaks, CA 91403
Harvey Art, president

Harmon, Merle Reid, Sr.
P.O. Box 1111
Arlington, TX 76010
Sportscaster

Harper, Valerie
8730 Sunset Blvd., 6th Floor
Los Angeles, CA 90069
Actress

Harper & Row Publishers, Inc.
10 E. 53rd St.
New York, NY 10022
Winthrop Knowlton, chairman

Harrington, Pat
2259 Linda Flora Dr.
Los Angeles, CA 90077
Actor

Harris, Barbara
c/o Robinson & Associates Inc.
132 S. Rodeo Dr.
Beverly Hills, CA 90212
Actress

Harris, Ellen Gandy
1077 Race St.
Denver, CO 80206
Civic worker

Harris, Emmylou
Box 2689
Danbury, CT 06813
Country singer, songwriter

Harris, Franco
400 W. North Ave.
Pittsburgh, PA 15212
Former football player

Harris, Jean
Bedford Hills Correctional Facility
Westchester County
Bedford Hills, NY 10507
Convicted murderer of Dr. Her-
man Tarnower, author of The
Complete Scarsdale Medical Diet

Harris, Joe Frank
391 W. Paces Ferry Rd.
NW. Atlanta, GA 30305
Governor of Georgia

Harris, Julie
c/o William Morris Agency
1350 Ave. of the Americas
New York, NY 10019
Actress

Harris, Richard
c/o New World Pictures Worldwide Publicity
1440 S. Sepulveda Blvd.
Los Angeles, CA 90025
Actor

Harris, Rosemary Ann
c/o International Creative Management
40 W. 57th St.
New York, NY 10019
Actress

Harris, Sam
9465 Wilshire Blvd., Suite 424
Beverly Hills, CA 90212
Singer

Harrison, George
c/o Dark Horse Records
3300 Warner Blvd.
Burbank, CA 91505
*Musician, songwriter, formerly
with the Beatles*

Harrison, Gregory
151 El Camino Dr.
Beverly Hills, CA 90212
Actor

Harrison, Rex Cary
La Renadiere
Carsinje 1252
Geneva, Switzerland
Actor

Harry, Deborah Ann
c/o Press Relations, Chrysalis
Records
645 Madison Ave.
New York, NY 10022
Singer

Hart, Corey
1888 Century Park E., Suite 1400
Los Angeles, CA 90067
Pop singer, songwriter

Hart, Gary
U.S. Senate Offices
Washington, DC 20510
*U.S. senator, 1988 presidential
candidate*

Hart, John Lewis
c/o News America Syndicate
1703 Kaiser Ave.
Irvine, CA 92714
*Cartoonist, creator of
"Wizard of Id"*

Hart, Mary
151 El Camino Dr.
Beverly Hills, CA 90212
Cohost, Entertainment Tonight

Hartford, John Cowan
1016 16th Ave. S.
Nashville, TN 37212
Singer, songwriter

Hartley, Mariette
1888 Century Park E., Suite 1400
Los Angeles, CA 90067
Actress

Hartman, Arthur A.
U.S. Embassy
Ulitsa Chaykovskogo 19/21/23
Moscow, USSR
U.S. ambassador to USSR

Hartman, David
c/o Trascott, Alyson & Craig Inc.
222 Cedar Ln.
Teaneck, NJ 07666
Former baseball player, television personality

Hartman, Lisa
9145 Sunset Blvd., Suite 218
Los Angeles, CA 90069
Actress, singer

Hartsfield, Henry Warren, Jr.
c/o NASA Lyndon B. Johnson
Space Center
Astronaut Office, Code CB
Houston, TX 77058
Astronaut

Harvey, Paul
360 N. Michigan Ave.
Chicago, IL 60601
Radio commentator, author, columnist

Haskell, Peter Abraham
c/o Belson-Klass Associates
211 S. Beverly Dr., Suite 107
Beverly Hills, CA 90212
Actor

Haskins, George Lee
P.O. Box 760
Paoli, PA 19301
Lawyer, educator

King Hassan II
Royal Palace
Rabat, Morocco
King of Morocco

Hasselhoff, David
P.O. Box 219
Downey, CA 90241
Actor

Hasting, Donald Francis
c/o CBS Public Relations Dept.
51 W. 52nd St.
New York, NY 10019
Actor, writer

Hatch, Orrin Grany
Russell Senate Office Bldg.
Room 135
Washington, DC 20510
U.S. senator

Hatch, Richard
11726 San Vicente Blvd.
Suite 300
Los Angeles, CA 90049
Actor

Hatfield, Mark
Room SH-711, U.S. Senate
Washington, DC 20510
U.S. senator

Haunt Hunters
963 Clayton Rd.
Ballwin, MO 63011
Phil Goodwin

Hawke, Robert J. L.
Office of the Prime Minister
Canberra, Australia
Prime minister of Australia

Hawkins, Joseph Elmer, Jr.
4004 E. Joy Rd.
Ann Arbor, MI 48105
Acoustic physiologist

Hawkins, Paula
Hart Senate Office Bldg.
Room 313
Washington, DC 20510
U.S. senator

Hawn, Goldie
1888 Century Park E., Suite 1400
Los Angeles, CA 90067
Actress

Hayden, Mike
Office of the Governor
State Capitol
Topeka, KS 66612-1590
Governor of Kansas

Hayden, Tom
State Capitol, Room 2141
Sacramento, CA 95814
State legislator, author, Jane Fonda's husband

Hayes, Elvin
c/o Houston Rockets, The Summit
10 Greenway Plaza E.
Houston, TX 77046
Basketball player

Hayes, Isaac
c/o Polydor Records Inc.
810 7th Ave.
New York, NY 10019
Composer, singer

Hayes, Lester
c/o Los Angeles Raiders
332 Center St.
El Segundo, CA 90245
Football player

Hayes, Peter Lind
3538 Pueblo Way
Las Vegas, NV 89109
Actor

Hayes, Susan Seaforth
6430 Sunset Blvd.
Hollywood, CA 90028
Actress

Hays, Kathryn
211 E. 70th St.
New York, NY 10021
Actress

H. B. Fuller Co.
2400 Kasota Ave.
St. Paul, MN 55108
E. L. Anderson, chairman and CEO. Makers of the Fuller Brush

Hearell, Janis
P.O. Box 1245
Greenwich, CT 06836
President, Advance Work Ltd.
Company advises, plans, and or-
chestrates special occasions and
large events

Hearns, Thomas
c/o Emanuel Steward
19600 W. McNichol St.
Detroit, MI 48219
Boxer

Hearst Corp.
959 8th Ave.
New York, NY 10019
Randolph A. Hearst, chairman

Heart
c/o Frontline Management
80 Universal City Plaza
Universal City, CA 91608
Rock band

Heaton, Bill
510 Montauk Highway
West Islip, NY 11795
President, Bridal Expos, Inc.,
operating the largest traveling
bridal show in the world

Hecht, Chic
Hart Senate Office Bldg.
Room 302
Washington, DC 20510
U.S. senator

Heckart, Eileen
c/o Bauman Hiller & Associates
9220 Sunset Blvd.
Los Angeles, CA 90069
Actress

Heckler, Margaret Mary
American Embassy, c/o Dept. of
State
Washington, DC 20120
Ambassador to Ireland

Hedgecock, Roger Allan
202 "C" St.
San Diego, CA 92101
Mayor of San Diego

Hedison, David Albert
c/o Nanas, Stern, Biers & Co.
9454 Wilshire Blvd.
Beverly Hills, CA 90212
Actor

Heffernan, Nathan Stewart
State Capitol
Madison, WI 53702
Chief justice, Wisconsin Supreme
Court

Heflin, Howell Thomas
Hart Senate Office Bldg.
Room 725
Washington, DC 20510
Lawyer, U.S. senator, former chief
justice of the Supreme Court of
Alabama

Hefner, Hugh Marston
c/o Playboy Enterprises
919 N. Michigan Ave.
Chicago, IL 60611
*Chairman of the board, Playboy
Enterprises*

Heineken, Alfred Henry
Heineken Breweries
NV Postbox 28 1000 AA
Amsterdam, Netherlands
President of Heineken Breweries

Heinlein, Robert
432 Park Ave. S., Suite 1205
New York, NY 10016
Author

Heinz, Henry John III
Russell Senate Office Bldg.
Room 277
Washington, DC 20510
U.S. senator

HJ Heinz Co.
P.O. Box 57
Pittsburgh, PA 15230

**Helene Curtis Industries,
Inc.**
325 N. Wells St.
Chicago, IL 60604
Gerald Gidwitz, chairman

Heller, Ann Williams
1100 Madison Ave.
New York, NY 10028
Writer, nutritionist

Heller, Joseph
c/o Simon & Schuster Press
Relations
630 5th Ave.
New York, NY 10020
Writer

Helmond, Katherine
151 El Camino Dr.
Beverly Hills, CA 90212
Actress

Helms, Jesse
Dirksen Senate Office Bldg.
Room 409
Washington, DC 20510
U.S. senator

Heloise
c/o King Features Syndicate
235 E. 45th St.
New York, NY 10017
Columnist, lecturer, broadcaster

Hemingway, Mariel
c/o Sam's Cafe
1406 3rd Ave.
New York, NY 10021
Actress

Hemlock Society
P.O. Box 66218
Los Angeles, CA 90066
Derek Humphrey

**Hemphill, Bernice
Monohan**
270 Masonic Ave.
San Francisco, CA 94118
Association exec., civic leader

Hemsley, Sherman
c/o Kenny Johnston
6920 Sunset Blvd., Suite 1002
Los Angeles, CA 90069
Actor

Henderson, Florence
9200 Sunset Blvd., Suite 1200
Los Angeles, CA 90069
Actress

Henderson, Ricky Henley
New York Yankees, Yankee
Stadium
Bronx, NY 10451
Baseball player

Henner, Marilu
100 S. Doheny Dr., Suite 1004
Los Angeles, CA 90048
Actress

Henning, Doug
10100 Santa Monica Blvd.
Suite 348
Los Angeles, CA 90067
Illusionist

**Henson, Jim
(James Maury Henson)**
117 E. 69th St.
New York, NY 10021
Creator of the Muppets

Hepburn, Audrey
c/o Kurt Frings
9440 Santa Monica Blvd.
Beverly Hills, CA 90210
Actress

**Herbert, Donald Jeffery
(Mr. Wizard)**
P.O. Box 83
Canoga Park, CA 91305
Motion picture and television producer and performer

Herbert, Michael Kinzly
1020 Church St.
Evanston, IL 60201
Magazine editor

Herbst, Dr. Lawrence
P.O. Box 3842
Houston, TX 77253-3842
Creator and distributor of portable radar dishes

Herder, Gerhard
German Democratic Republic
Embassy
1717 Massachusetts Ave. NW.
Washington, DC 20036
German Democratic Republic ambassador to the U.S.

Herman, Jerry
c/o ASCAP
One Lincoln Plaza
New York, NY 10023
Composer and lyricist

Herman, Pee Wee
P.O. Box 48243
Los Angeles, CA 90048
Entertainer

Hernandez, Keith
New York Mets, Shea Stadium
Roosevelt Ave. and 126th St.
Flushing, NY 11368
Baseball player

Hernandez, Willie
Detroit Tigers, Tiger Stadium
Detroit, MI 48216
Baseball player

Hernandez-Colon, Rafael
Commonwealth Capitol Senate La
Fortaleza
San Juan, PR 00901
Governor of Puerto Rico

Herrmann, Edward Kirk
c/o International Creative
Management
40 W. 57th St.
New York, NY 10019
Actor

Hershey, Barbara
1888 Century Park E., Suite 1400
Los Angeles, CA 90067
Actress

Hershey Food Corp.
P.O. Box 814
Hershey, PA 17033
Richard A. Zimmerman,
chairman and CEO

Hershler, Edgar J.
Office of the Governor,
Capitol Bldg.
Cheyenne, WY 82002
Governor of Wyoming

The Hertz Corp.
660 Madison Ave.
New York, NY 10021
Frank A. Olsen,
chairman and CEO

Herzog, Whitey
(Dorrel Norman Elvert
Herzog)
St. Louis Cardinals, Busch Memo-
rial Stadium
250 Stadium Plaza
St. Louis, MO 63102
Baseball manager

Hesseman, Howard
151 El Camino Dr.
Beverly Hills, CA 90212
Actor

Heston, Charlton
8730 Sunset Blvd., 6th Floor
Los Angeles, CA 90067
Actor

Hewlett-Packard Co.
3000 Hanover St.
Palo Alto, CA 94304
David Packard, chairman

Heyerdahl, Thor
Colla Micheri
Laigueglia, Italy
Anthropologist, explorer, author

Hidalgo, Edward
1828 "L" St. NW., Suite 1111
Washington, DC 20036
Lawyer, former secretary of the
U.S. Navy Department

Higgins, Colin
1888 Century Park E., Suite 1400
Los Angeles, CA 90067
Writer and director

Higgins, Dick
P.O. Box 27
Tarrytown, NY 10591
Author, publisher

Higgins, Jack
c/o David Higham Associates
5-8 Lower John St.
Golden Square
London W1R 4HA England
Author

Hilburn, Robert
c/o Los Angeles Times
Times-Mirror Square
Los Angeles, CA 90053
Pop music critic

Hiliery, Patrick J.
Office of the President
Dublin, Ireland
President of Ireland

Hill, Arthur
1888 Century Park E., Suite 1400
Los Angeles, CA 90067
Actor

Hill, Benny
2 Queens Gate, Flat 7
London SW7 England
Comedian

Hill, Drew
P.O. Box 1516
Houston, TX 77001
Football player

Hill, George Roy
c/o Pan Arts Productions Corp.
4000 Warner Blvd.
Burbank, CA 90048
Motion picture director

Hill, Walter
8899 Beverly Blvd.
Los Angeles, CA 90048
Motion picture writer and director

Hiller, Arthur
c/o Phil Gersh Agency, Inc.
222 N. Canon Dr.
Beverly Hills, CA 90210
Motion picture director

Hiller, Wendy
c/o International Creative
Management
388/396 Oxford St.
London W1 England
Actress

Hillerman, John Benedict
9200 Sunset Blvd., Suite 1009
Los Angeles, CA 90069
Actor

Hills Bros. Coffee, Inc.
2 Harrison St.
San Francisco, CA 94105
P. J. Miller, chairman

Hilton Hotels Corp.
9336 Santa Monica Blvd.
Beverly Hills, CA 90210
Barron Hilton, president and CEO

Hinckley, John, Jr.
St. Elizabeth's Hospital
2700 Martin Luther King Ave.
Washington, DC 20005
Convicted for attempted assassination of President Reagan

Hipple, Eric
1200 Featherstone Rd.
Box 4200
Pontiac, MI 48057
Football player

Emperor Hirohito
Office of Emperor
Tokyo, Japan
Emperor of Japan

Hirsch, Judd
15760 Ventura Blvd., Suite 1730
Encino, CA 91436
Actor

Ho, Don
2005 Kalia Rd.
Honolulu, HI 96815
Entertainer

Hodgman, Joan Elizabeth
494 Stanford Dr.
Arcadia, CA 91006
Neonatologist

Hoeffner, Betty
40 Skokie Blvd., Number 30
Northbrook, IL 60062
President, Tank Goodness. Company designs and maintains aquariums, offering a wide range of services

Hoffman, Dustin
1888 Century Park E., Suite 1400
Los Angeles, CA 90067
Actor

Hogan, Ben
c/o Ben Hogan Co.
2912 W. Pafford St.
Fort Worth, TX 76110
Golfer, business exec.

Holbrook, Hal
10000 Santa Monica Blvd.
Suite 305
Los Angeles, CA 90067
Actor

Holder, Geoffrey
c/o Donald Buchwald Associates
10 E. 44th St.
New York, NY 10017
Dancer, actor, choreographer, director

Holiday, Jennifer
9000 Sunset Blvd., Suite 315
Los Angeles, CA 90069
Actress

Holiday Corp.
1023 Cherry Rd.
Memphis, TN 38117
Michael D. Rose,
chairman and CEO

Holland, Arthur John
203 Buckingham Ave.
Trenton, NJ 08618
Mayor of Trenton

Holliday, Polly Dean
9255 Sunset Blvd., Suite 505
Los Angeles, CA 90069
Actress

Holliman, Earl
8899 Beverly Blvd.
Los Angeles, CA 90048
Actor

Hollings, Earnest Frederick
Russell Senate Office Bldg.
Room 125
Washington, DC 20510
U.S. senator

The Hollywood Reporter
6715 Sunset Blvd.
Los Angeles, CA 90028
Tichi Wilkerson, president, pub-
lisher, and editor-in-chief

Holm, Celeste
c/o Mishkin Agency
9255 Sunset Blvd.
Los Angeles, CA 90069
Actress

Holmes, Francis William
c/o Shade Tree Labs
U. of Massachusetts
Amherst, MA 01002
Plant pathologist

Holmes, Larry
c/o Holmes Enterprises, Inc.
704 Alpha Bldg.
Easton, PA 18042
Boxer

Holt, Stephen S.
Goddard Space Flight Center
Code 660
Greenbelt, MD 20770
Astrophysicist

Holt, Victoria
c/o Doubleday & Co.
Garden City, NY 11530
Author

Homer, William Innes
Department of Art History,
U. of Delaware
Newark, DE 19711
Author, educator

Honecker, Erich
Office of the Chairman
Berlin, East Germany
Chairman of Council of State,
East Germany

Honeywell, Inc.
Honeywell Plaza
Minneapolis, MN 55408
Edson W. Spencer, chairman

Hooker, John Lee
P.O. Box 210103
San Francisco, CA 94121
Singer, guitarist

Hookstraten, Ed
9012 Beverly Blvd.
Los Angeles, CA 90048
Newscasters' manager

The Hoover Co.
101 E. Maple St.
North Canton, OH 44720
*Merle R. Rawson,
chairman and CEO*

Hope, Bob
3808 Riverside Dr.
Burbank, CA 91505
Entertainer

Hopkins, Anthony
151 El Camino Dr.
Beverly Hills, CA 90212
Actor

Hopper, Dennis
10000 Santa Monica Blvd.
Suite 305
Los Angeles, CA 90067
*Actor, writer, photographer,
film director*

Horan, Hume Alexander
American Embassy
APO New York, NY 09668
Ambassador

Horgan, Paul
Wesleyan University
Middletown, CT 06457
Author, educator

Horn, Paul Joseph
P.O. Box 6193, Station C
Victoria, BC. V8P 5L5
Canada
Musician

Horne, Lena
1200 S. Arlington Ave.
Los Angeles, CA 90024
Singer

Hornsby, Bruce
c/o Tim Neece Management
10513 Cushdon St.
Los Angeles, CA 90064
Singer, songwriter, musician

Horovitz, Israel Arthur
c/o Writers & Artists Agency
162 W. 56th St.
New York, NY 10019
Playwright

Horowitz, David Charles
P.O. Box 49740
Los Angeles, CA 90049
Consumer commentator

Horowitz, Vladimir
c/o Columbia Artists Management
165 W. 57th St.
New York, NY 10019
Pianist

Horton, Robert Carlton
U.S. Bureau of Mines
2401 E St.
NW. Washington, DC 20241
Director, U.S. Bureau of Mines

Houdek, Robert G.
Department of State
Embassy to Uganda
Washington, DC 20520
U.S. ambassador to Uganda

Houston, Whitney
c/o Galaxy Artists
410 E. 50th St.
New York, NY 10022
Singer

Howard, Ken
1888 Century Park E., Suite 1400
Los Angeles, CA 90067
Actor

Howard, Ron
10351 Santa Monica Blvd., 2nd
Floor
Los Angeles, CA 90025
Actor, director

Howard Johnson Co.
One Howard Johnson Plaza
Boston, MA 02125
G. Michael Hostage, chairman

Howe, Gordon
c/o Hartford Whalers
One Civic Center Plaza
Hartford, CT 06103
Hockey player

Hoyt, Dewey Lamarr
P.O. Box 2000
San Diego, CA 92120
Baseball player

Hubbard, David
P.O. Box 62429
Los Angeles, CA 90062
Chief operating officer, Cops Unlimited, a crime prevention organization consulting in all fields

Hubley, John
c/o Hubley Studio, Inc.
355 E. 50th St.
New York, NY 10022
Animator, motion picture producer and director

Hubley, Season
8500 Wilshire Blvd., Suite 506
Beverly Hills, CA 90211
Actress

Huddleston, Walter Darlington
Dirksen Senate Office Bldg.,
Room 262
Washington, DC 20510
U.S. senator

Hudnut, William Herbert III
2501 City County Bldg.
Indianapolis, IN 46204
Mayor of Indianapolis, Indiana

Hughes, Barnard
c/o International Creative
Management
40 W. 57th St.
New York, NY 10019
Actor

Hughes, Harry Roe
Office of the Governor, State
House
Annapolis, MD 21404
Governor of Maryland

Hughes, John
8899 Beverly Blvd.
Los Angeles, CA 90048
*Motion picture writer and
director*

Hughes, Stanley John
c/o Biosystematics Research
Institute
Central Experimental Farm
Ottawa, ON. K1A OC6
Canada
Mycologist

Hughes, Ted
c/o Harper & Row
10 E. 53rd St.
New York, NY 10022
Poet, author

Huie, William Bradford
P.O. Box 1567
Scottsboro, AL 35768
Author

Hulswit, Mart
c/o CBS-TV Press Relations
51 W. 52nd St.
New York, NY 10019
Actor

Human League
c/o Tom Mohler, Sanctuary Music
6777 Hollywood Blvd., 6th Floor
Hollywood, CA 90028
Pop music group

Humbard, Rex
1745 Merriman Rd., Number 300
Akron, OH 44313-5251
Televangelist

Humphrey, Gordon John
U.S. Senate
Washington, DC 20510
U.S. senator

Hunt, James Baxter, Jr.
Governor's Office
Raleigh, NC 27611
Governor of North Carolina

Hunter, James Graham
Lindenshade
42 Clonavor Rd.
Silver Spring Park, West Orange,
NJ 07052
*Cartoonist, watercolorist, writer,
advertising producer*

Hunter, Catfish (Jim)
RR Number One, Box 945
Hertford, NC 27944
Former baseball player

Hunter, Ross
370 Trousdale Place
Beverly Hills, CA 90210
Motion picture producer

Hurley, Kathy
484 W. 3rd St., Number 22P
New York, NY 10012
Actress, playwright

Hurt, John
60 Saint James St.
London SW1 England
Actor

Hurt, William
10100 Santa Monica Blvd., 16th
Floor
Los Angeles, CA 90067
Actor

Husak, Gustav
Office of the President
Prague, Czechoslovakia
President of Czechoslovakia

King Hussein I
Box 1055
Amman, Jordan
King of Jordan

Hussein, Saddam
Office of the President
Baghdad, Iraq
President of Iraq

Hutton, Timothy
c/o Lookout Management
8919 Sunset Blvd.
Los Angeles, CA 90069
Actor

Hyatt Corp.
200 W. Madison
Chicago, IL 60606
*Jay A. Pritzker,
chairman and CEO*

Hyde-White, Wilfred
9200 Sunset Blvd., Suite 909
Los Angeles, CA 90069
Actor

Hyer, Martha
9200 Sunset Blvd.
Los Angeles, CA 90069
Actress

Hyman, Phyllis
1608 Walnut St., Box 50
Suite 1302
Philadelphia, PA 19103
Soul singer

**Iacocca, Lee
(Lido Anthony Iacocca)**
c/o Chrysler Corp.
12000 Chrysler Dr.
Highland Park, MI 48288
CEO, Chrysler Corporation

Ian, Janis
9200 Sunset Blvd., Suite 1102
Los Angeles, CA 90069
Singer, composer

Idol, Billy
200 W. 57th St., Suite 1403
New York, NY 10019
Pop singer, songwriter

**Iglesias, Julio
(Julio Jose Iglesias de la
Cueva)**
10000 Santa Monica Blvd.
Suite 400
Los Angeles, CA 90067
Singer, songwriter

Igloo Corp.
P.O. Box 19322
Houston, TX 77024
J. Futch, president

**Reverend Ike
(Frederick Joseph
Eikerenkoetter)**
4140 Broadway
New York, NY 10033
Evangelist, educator, lecturer

I Magnin
7 W. 7th St.
Cincinnati, OH 45202
*Howard Goldfeder,
chairman and CEO*

Ingels, Marty
c/o Ingels Inc.
8322 Beverly Blvd.
Hollywood, CA 90048
Agent, motion picture and television production exec.

Ingram, James
9200 Sunset Blvd., Suite 823
Los Angeles, CA 90069
Singer

Innerview, Inc.
8913 W. Olympic Blvd., Suite 201
Beverly Hills, CA 90211
Jack Morris, president

Inouye, Daniel Ken
Hart Senate Office Bldg.
Room 722
Washington, DC 20510
U.S. senator

International Business Machines (IBM)
Old Orchard Rd.
Armonk, NY 10504
John F. Akers, chairman

International Flavors and Fragrances, Inc.
521 W. 57th St.
New York, NY 10019
Eugene P. Grisanti, chairman and CEO

Invisible Empire, Knights of the Ku Klux Klan
P.O. Box 700
Five Points, AL 36855
Jim Blair

Iron Maiden
c/o International Creative Management
40 W. 57th St.
New York, NY 10019
Heavy metal rock group

Irons, Jeremy John
c/o Hutton Management
200 Fulham Rd.
London SW10 9PN England
Actor

Irving, John Winslow
c/o Random House
201 E. 50th St.
New York, NY 10022
Author

Irwin, Hale S.
2801 Stonington Pl.
St. Louis, MO 63131
Golfer

The Isley Brothers
c/o Ronald Isley
446 Liberty Rd.
Inglewood, NJ 07631
Rock and soul group

Issel, Dan
c/o Denver Nuggets,
McNichols Sports Arena
1635 Clay St.
Denver, CO 80204
Basketball player

ITT Corp.
320 Park Ave.
New York, NY 10022
Rand Araskog, chairman and CEO

Ittmann, Majorie McCullough
2353 Bedford Ave.
Cincinnati, OH 45208
Girl Scout official

Ives, Burl (Icle Ivanhoe)
427 N. Canon Dr., Suite 205
Beverly Hills, CA 90210
Singer, actor

Jack, Beau
c/o All Star Boxing Club
616 NE. 8th St.
Hallandale, FL 33009
*Lightweight boxer, member of
Boxing Hall of Fame*

Jack Daniel Distillery
Main Street
Lynchburg, TN 37352
*Martin S. Brown,
chairman and CEO*

Jack-in-the-Box Restaurants
9330 Balboa Ave.
San Diego, CA 92112
*Jack W. Goodall, Jr.,
chairman, president, and CEO*

Jackson, Freddie
c/o Hush Productions
231 W. 58th St.
New York, NY 10019
Soul singer, songwriter

Jackson, Glenda
8899 Beverly Blvd.
Los Angeles, CA 90048
Actress

Jackson, Janet
c/o John McClain, A&M Records
1416 N. La Brea Ave.
Hollywood, CA 90028
Pop singer, songwriter

Jackson, Rev. Jesse
930 E. 50th St.
Chicago, IL 60615
*Clergyman, civic leader, 1984 and
1988 presidential candidate*

Jackson, Joe
c/o A&M Records Press Relations
1416 N. La Brea Ave.
Hollywood, CA 90028
Musician, singer, songwriter

Jackson, Kate
1888 Century Park E., Suite 1400
Los Angeles, CA 90067
Actress

Jackson, Keith
c/o ABC Sports
1330 Ave. of the Americas
28th Floor
New York, NY 10019
Sports commentator, writer, producer

Jackson, Michael
c/o Frank Dileo Management
15830 Woodvale
Encino, CA 91436
Singer, songwriter

**Jackson, Reggie
(Reginald Martinez Jackson)**
200 State College Blvd.
Anaheim, CA 92806
Baseball player

Jackson, Robert
P.O. Box 5425
Santa Barbara, CA 93108
CEO, Jackson-Mitchell, Inc. Company produces Goat Milk, including evaporated, powdered, and unpasturized

Jacobi, Derek George
c/o International Creative Management
388-396 Oxford St.
London WIN 9HE England
Actor

Jacobi, Lou
c/o William Morris Agency
1350 Ave. of the Americas
New York, NY 10019
Actor

Jacobs, David
10202 W. Washington Blvd.
Culver City, CA 90230
Television producer, author

Jacobs, Woodrow Cooper
6000 Executive Bldg.
Rockville, MD 20852
Meteorologist, oceanographer

Jacobson, David
207 Beechwood Ave.
San Antonio, TX 78216
Rabbi

Jacuzzi, Inc.
11511 New Benton Highway
Little Rock, AR 72209
Raymond E. Horan, president

**Jagger, Mick
(Michael Phillip Jagger)**
c/o Mahoney/Wasserman
117 N. Robertson Blvd.
Los Angeles, CA 90048
Rock singer

Jahn, Sigmund
108 Berlin
Postfach 66650, DDR
Cosmonaut

Jakes, William
c/o Harcourt, Brace, Jovanovich
757 3rd Ave.
New York, NY 10017
Author

James, Peter
8500 Station St., Number 240
Mentor, OH 44060
President, Bingo Science magazine. Company publishes local bingo players' guide in different states

Janis, Conrad
c/o Korman Contemporary Artists Ltd.
132 Lasky Dr.
Beverly Hills, CA 90212
Actor, jazz musician, art dealer

Janklow, William John
State Capitol Bldg.
Pierre, SD 57501
Governor of South Dakota

Jantzen, Inc.
P.O. Box 3001
Portland, OR 97208
Jerome M. Pool, CEO

Jarreau, Al
c/o Patrick Rains
8752 Holloway Dr.
Los Angeles, CA 90069
Singer

Jarrett, Keith
c/o Vincent Ryan
135 W. 16th St.
New York, NY 10011
Pianist

Jarriel, Thomas Edwin
c/o ABC News
7 W. 66th St.
New York, NY 10022
ABC news correspondent

Jarrott, Charles
151 El Camino Dr.
Beverly Hills, CA 90212
Motion picture and television director

Jaruzelski, General Wojciech
Office of the Premier
Warsaw, Poland
Premier of Poland

Jarvik, Dr. Robert
825 N. 300 West St.
Salt Lake City, UT 84103
Inventor of artificial heart

Jarvis, Graham Powley
c/o Lionel Larner Ltd.
9200 Sunset Blvd.
Los Angeles, CA 90069
Actor

Jaworski, Ronald Vincent
c/o Philadelphia Eagles,
Veterans Stadium
Philadelphia, PA 19148
Football player

J. C. Penney Co., Inc.
1301 Ave. of the Americas
New York, NY 10019
*William R. Howell,
chairman and CEO*

Jefferson, John Larry
c/o Cleveland Brows, Cleveland
Stadium
Cleveland, OH 44114
Football player

Jehovah's Witnesses
c/o Watchtower Bible and Tract
Society of New York, Inc.
25 Columbia Heights
Brooklyn, NY 11201
Frederick W. Franz, president

Jellybean
1888 Century Park E., Suite 1400
Los Angeles, CA 90067
Music producer, songwriter

Jemima, Aunt
P.O. Box 9001
Chicago, IL 60609
*Breakfast food mascot, makes a
mean plate of pancakes*

Jenkins, Ferguson Arthur
c/o Chicago Cubs, Wrigley Field
North Clark and Addison Sts.
Chicago, IL 60613
Baseball player

Jennings, Peter Charles
c/o ABC Press Relations
1330 Ave. of the Americas, 7W-7
New York, NY 10019
*Anchorman, ABC World News
Tonight*

Jennings, Peter Randolph
c/o The Rockefeller Foundation
1133 Ave. of the Americas
New York, NY 10036
*Tropical agriculturalist, rice
breeder*

Jennings, Waylon
c/o Mark Rothbaum & Associates,
Inc.
225 Main St.
Danbury, CT 06811
Country western musician

Jensen, Rue L.
1712 W. Vine Dr.
Fort Collins, CO 80521
Animal pathologist, educator

Jepsen, Roger William
U.S. Senate Offices
Washington, DC 20510
U.S. senator

Jethro Tull
12 Stratford Pl.
London W1N 9AF England
Rock band

The Jets
c/o Don Powell Management
708 N. 1st St., Suite 135
Minneapolis, MN 55401
Pop music group

Jett, Joan
c/o Jett Lag
155 E. 55th St., Suite 6H
New York, NY 10022
Rock guitarist, singer, songwriter

Jillian, Ann
P.O. Box 408
San Ramon, CA 94583
Actress

Jim & Jesse
404 Shoreline Dr.
Tallahassee, FL 32301
Bluegrass musicians

**Jimmy the Greek
(Synodinos Demetrios
Georgos)**
Omni Park Hotel
56th and 7th Aves., Suite 2049
New York, NY 10019
Oddsmaker, columnist

Jockey International, Inc.
2300 60th St.
Kenosha, WI 53140
*Donna W. Steigerwaldt,
chairman and CEO*

**Joel, Billy (William Martin
Joel)**
c/o Frank Management, Inc.
375 N. Broadway
Jericho, NY 11753
Musician, songwriter

Joffe, Charles
c/o Rollins, Joffe, Morra & Brezner, Paramount Studios
5555 Melrose Ave.
Los Angeles, CA 90038
*Motion picture producer, comedy
management executive*

**Joffrey, Robert
(Abdullah Jaffa Bey Khan)**
434 6th Ave.
New York, NY 10019
*Director, choreographer, the Jof-
frey Ballet*

**John, Elton
(Reginald Kenneth
Dwight)**
c/o John Reid, Constant Commu-
nications
51 Holland St., 2nd Floor
London, W8 7JB England
Pop star

John, Thomas Edward, Jr.
New York Yankees, Yankee
Stadium
Bronx, NY 10451
Baseball player

The John Birch Society
395 Concord Ave.
Belmont, MA 02178
Charles J. Humphries

Johncock, Gordon Walter
715 S. Fall River Dr.
Coldwater, MI 49036
Race car driver

**John Hancock Mutual Life
Insurance Co.**
John Hancock Plaza
Boston, MA 02116
*John G. McElwee,
chairman and CEO*

**John Paul II, His Holiness
the Pope (Karol Jozef
Wojtyla)**
Palazzo Apostolico
Vatican City, Italy
Pope of the Catholic Church

Johnson, Arte
c/o Richard Lawrence
301 N. San Vicente Blvd.
Los Angeles, CA 90048
Comedian

Johnson, Bob
P.O. Box 1540 Station M
Calgary AB T2P 3B9
Canada
Coach, Calgary Flames hockey team

Johnson, Dennis
c/o Boston Celtics
North Station, Boston Garden
Boston, MA 02114
Basketball player

Johnson, Don
3575 Cahuenga W., Suite 470
Los Angeles, CA 90068
Actor, rock singer

Johnson, Francis Benjamin
Herb Tobias & Associates
1901 Ave. of the Stars
Los Angeles, CA 90067
Actor

Johnson, Jesse
10100 Santa Monica Blvd., 16th
Floor
Los Angeles, CA 90069
Guitarist, singer, songwriter

Johnson, Kenneth Owen
18630 Polvera Dr.
San Diego, CA 92128
Audiologist, exec.

**Johnson, Lady Bird
(Claudia Atta Taylor,
Mrs. Lyndon B. Johnson)**
LBJ Library, 2313 Red River
Austin, TX 78705
Former first lady

**Johnson, Magic
(Earvin Johnson)**
P.O. Box 10
The Forum
Inglewood, CA 90306
Basketball player

Johnson, Marques Kevin
c/o Milwaukee Bucks
901 N. 4th St.
Milwaukee, WI 53203
Basketball player

Johnson, Rafer Lewis
c/o The Mishkin Agency
9255 Sunset Blvd.
Los Angeles, CA 90069
Actor, athlete, telephone company exec.

Johnson, Robert Ivar
3622 Dana Shores Dr.
Tampa, FL 33614
Business exec.

Johnson, Ron ("Toto")
c/o Ringling Bros. & Barnum &
Bailey Circus, Red Unit
Clown Alley, 3201 New Mexico
Ave. NW.
Washington, DC 20016
Circus clown

Johnson, Roy E.
1125 17th St. NW.
Washington, DC 20036
President, United Union of Roofers, Waterproofers, and Allied Workers

Johnson, Van
151 El Camino Dr.
Beverly Hills, CA 90212
Actor

Johnson, William Alexander
Louisiana State University,
Dept. of Poultry Science
Baton Rouge, LA 70803
Poultry science educator

Johnson & Johnson
Johnson & Johnson Plaza
New Brunswick, NJ 08933
*James E. Burke,
chairman and CEO*

Johnson-Masters, Virginia
24 S. Kingshighway
St. Louis, MO 63108
Psychologist, author, expert on sex

Johnston, J. Bennett
Hart Senate Office Bldg.
Room 136
Washington, DC 20510
U.S. senator

Jones, Dean Caroll
132 Lasky Dr.
Beverly Hills, CA 90212
Actor

Jones, Elvin Ray
c/o Palo Alto Records
11026 Ventura Blvd., Suite 2
Studio City, CA 91604
Recording artist

Jones, George
c/o Triad Artists, Inc.
9200 Sunset Blvd., Suite 823
Los Angeles, CA 90069
Country singer and songwriter

Jones, Grace
Box 82
Great Neck, NY 11022
Model, singer, actress

Jones, Howard
c/o International Talent Group
200 W. 57th St., Suite 1403
New York, NY 10019
Pop music singer, keyboardist, songwriter

Jones, James Earl
c/o Bauman, Hiller & Associates
9220 Sunset Blvd.
Los Angeles, CA 90069
Actor

Jones, Jennifer
P.O. Box 367
Malibu, CA 90265
Actress

Jones, K. C.
c/o Boston Celtics, Boston
Garden
North Station
Boston, MA 02114
*Coach, Boston Celtics basketball
team*

Jones, Quincy
9200 Sunset Blvd., Suite 823
Los Angeles, CA 90069
*Musician, composer, record pro-
ducer*

Jones, Shirley
132 Lasky Dr.
Beverly Hills, CA 90212
Actress, singer

Jones, Terry
Python Productions
6 Cambridge Gate
London NW1 England
*Film director, author, member of
Monty Python comedy troupe*

Jones, Tom
10100 Santa Monica Blvd.
Suite 205
Los Angeles, CA 90067
Singer

Jong, Erica Mann
c/o Morton L. Janklow Associates
598 Madison Ave.
New York, NY 10022
Author, poet

**Jordan, Hamilton (William
Hamilton McWorter Jor-
dan)**
1100 Spring St., Suite 450
Atlanta, GA 30344
*Chief of staff for former President
Jimmy Carter*

Jordan, Robert Henry
State Judicial Bldg.
Atlanta, GA 30334
*Chief justice, Supreme Court of
Georgia*

Jorio, Maati
Embassy of Kingdom of Morocco
1601 21st St.
NW. Washington, DC 20009
Moroccan ambassador to U.S.

Jourdan, Louis
8899 Beverly Blvd.
Los Angeles, CA 90048
Actor

Journey
P.O. Box 404
San Francisco, CA 94101
Rock band

Jovan, Inc.
980 N. Michigan Ave.
Chicago, IL 60611
Richard E. Meyer, president

Joy, James, Jr.
815 16th St. NW.
Washington, DC 20006
*President, Utility Workers Union
of America*

THE ADDRESS BOOK

Judas Priest
c/o Premier Talent Agency
3 E. 54th St.
New York, NY 10022
Heavy metal rock band

The Judds
P.O. Box 17325
Nashville, TN 37217
Country music singers

Judson, Lyman Spicer Vincent
P.O. Box 277
Rochester, MN 55901
Author, artist

**Julia, Raul
(Raul Rafael Carlos Julia)**
c/o Susan J. Wright
449 E. 84th St., 4A
New York, NY 10028
Actor

Jump, Gordon
c/o Writers & Artists Agency
11726 San Vicente Blvd.
Suite 300
Los Angeles, CA 90049
Actor

Jurgensen, Christian Adolph III
7525 NW. 37th Ave.
Miami, FL 33147
Sports commentator

Kael, Pauline
c/o The New Yorker
25 W. 43rd St.
New York, NY 10036
Author, film critic

Kagan, Jeremy Paul
9200 Sunset Blvd., Penthouse 25
Los Angeles, CA 90069
Filmmaker

Kahn, Michael
One W. 72nd St.
New York, NY 10023
Stage director

**Kaiser Aluminum &
Chemical Corp.**
300 Lakeside Dr.
Oakland, CA 94612
*Cornell C. Maier,
chairman and CEO*

Kalb, Marvin Leonard
c/o NBC News
30 Rockefeller Plaza
New York, NY 10112
*Radio and television news corre-
spondent*

Kalin, Jeff
34 Judson Ln.
Bethlehem, CT 06751
*President, Primitive Technologies,
Inc. Creates replicas of Native
American goods using authentic
materials*

Kal Kan Foods, Inc.
3386 E. 44th St.
Vernon, CA 90058
John Barrow, president

Kamali, Norma
11 W. 56th St.
New York, NY 10019
Fashion designer

Kamen, Stan
151 El Camino Dr.
Beverly Hills, CA 90212
Theatrical producer

Kampleman, Max M.
3154 Highland Pl.
NW. Washington, DC 20008
*Head of U.S. delegation to negoti-
ations on nuclear and space arms*

Kanaly, Steven Francis
P.O. Box 8086
Calabasas, CA 91302
Actor

Kander, John
c/o Dramatists Guild
234 W. 44th St.
New York, NY 10036
Composer

Kane, Carol
1888 Century Park E., Suite 1400
Los Angeles, CA 90067
Actress

Kane, Robert Francis
U.S. Ambassador to Ireland,
c/o Dept. of State
Washington, DC 20520
U.S. ambassador to Ireland

Kansas
c/o Carr Company
19528 Ventura Blvd., Suite 361
Tarzana, CA 91356
Rock band

Kantner, Paul
P.O. Box 15-584
San Francisco, CA 94115
Rock singer, songwriter, guitarist

Kaplan, Gabriel
9220 Sunset Blvd., Garden Suite B
Los Angeles, CA 90069
Actor, comedian

Kaplan, Stanley Henry
c/o Stanley Kaplan Educational
Center
131 W. 56th St.
New York, NY 10019
*Founder, Stan Kaplan Educational
Center*

Karamanlis, Constantine
Office of the President
Athens, Greece
President of Greece

Karawina, Erica
3529 Akaka Pl.
Honolulu, HI 96822
Painter, stained glass designer

Karmal, Babrak
Office of the President
Kabul, Afghanistan
President of Afghanistan

Karras, Alex
151 El Camino Dr.
Beverly Hills, CA 90212
Actor

Kasdan, Lawrence Edward
9665 Wilshire Blvd., Suite 900
Beverly Hills, CA 90212
Motion picture writer, director

Kasiwihara, Ken
c/o ABC News
277 Golden Gate
San Francisco, CA 94102
Television journalist

Kassebaum, Nancy Landon
302 Russell Senate Office Bldg.
Washington, DC 20510
U.S. senator

Kassel, Virginia Wettmer
c/o Prime Time Entertainment, Inc.
485 Madison Ave.
New York, NY 10022
Television producer

Kasten, Paul Rudolph
P.O. Box X
Oak Ridge, TN 37830
Nuclear engineer

Kasten, Robert W., Jr.
Hart Senate Office Bldg.
Room 110
Washington, DC 20510
U.S. senator

Katz, Hilda
915 West End Ave., Apt. 5D
New York, NY 10025
Artist

Katz, Julian
c/o Gastrointestinal Specialists
555 City Ave.
Bala-Cynwyd, PA 19004
Gastroenterologist and educator

Katz, Ray
9255 Sunset Blvd., Suite 115
Los Angeles, CA 90069
Personal manager, producer

Kavalek, Lubomir
11002 Saffold Way
Reston, VA 22090
Chess expert

Kawasaki Motors Corp., U.S.A.
9950 Jeronimo Rd.
Irvine, CA 92718
M. Tazaki, president

Kaye, Alex R.
1074 Independence Ave.
Mountain View, CA 94043
President, Porta-Bote-International. Makes 8-, 10-, and 12-foot boats that fold to 4 inches flat

**Kazan, Lainie
(Lainie Levine)**
9903 Santa Monica Blvd.
Number 283
Beverly Hills, CA 90212
Singer

Keach, Stacy, Jr.
1875 Century Park E., Suite 1600
Los Angeles, CA 90067-2517
Actor, writer, director, producer

Keach, Stacy, Sr.
5216 Laurel Canyon Blvd.
North Hollywood, CA 91607
Producer, director

Kean, Thomas H.
c/o Carl Golden, Room 112
State House
Trenton, NJ 08625
Governor of New Jersey

Keane, Bill
c/o Cowles Syndicate, Inc.
715 Locust St.
Des Moines, IA 50309
*Cartoonist, creator of "Family
Circus"*

Kearney, Joseph Laurence
Western Athletic Conference
14 W. Dry Creek Circle
Littleton, CO 80120
Athletic conference administrator

Keating, Thomas Arthur
706 Pacific St.
Alameda, CA 94501
Football player

Keaton, Diane
c/o Stan Kamen, William Morris
Agency
1350 Ave. of the Americas
New York, NY 10019
Actress

Keaton, Michael
1888 Century Park E., Suite 1400
Los Angeles, CA 90067
Actor

Keebler Co.
One Hollow Tree Ln.
Elmhurst, IL 60126
*Thomas M. Garvin,
president and CEO*

Keel
c/o Gold Mountain Records
1416 N. La Brea Ave.
Los Angeles, CA 90028
Rock group

Keeshan, Bob
c/o International Creative
Management
40 W. 57th St.
New York, NY 10019
Clarabell on Howdy Doody

Keith, Brian
c/o James McHugh Agency
8150 Beverly Blvd., Suite 303
Los Angeles, CA 90048
Actor

Kell, George Clyde
c/o Detroit Tigers, Tiger Stadium
Detroit, MI 48216
*Broadcaster, former baseball
player*

Keller, Marthe
151 El Camino Dr.
Beverly Hills, CA 90212
Actress

Kellerman, Sally Claire
1888 Century Park E., Suite 1400
Los Angeles, CA 90067
Actress

**Kelley, DeForest
(Jackson DeForest Kelley)**
c/o Camden Agency
409 N. Camden Dr.
Beverly Hills, CA 90210
Actor

Kellogg, William Welch
National Center for Atmospheric
Research
Boulder, CO 80307
Meteorologist

Kellogg Co.
P.O. Box 3599
Battle Creek, MI 49016
*William E. LaMothe,
chairman and CEO*

Kelly, Gene Curran
8899 Beverly Blvd.
Los Angeles, CA 90048
Dancer, actor, director

Kelly, Lucie Stirm Young
600 W. 168th St.
New York, NY 10032
Nursing educator

Kelly Services, Inc.
999 W. Big Beaver Rd.
Troy, MI 48084
*William R. Kelly, chairman. Home
of the Kelly Girl*

Kemp, Jack F.
2252 Rayburn House Office Bldg.
Washington, DC 20510
*U.S. senator, 1988 presidential
candidate*

Kemper, Victor Jay
10313 W. Pico Blvd.
Los Angeles, CA 90064
Cinematographer

Kennedy, Edward Moore
Senate Office Bldg.
Washington, DC 20510
U.S. senator

Kennedy, George
132 Lasky Dr.
Beverly Hills, CA 90212
Actor

Kennedy, Rose Fitzgerald
Hyannis Port, MA 02647
*Mother of John, Edward, and
Robert Kennedy*

Kenny G
10100 Santa Monica Blvd.
16th Floor
Los Angeles, CA 90069
Musician, songwriter

**Kentucky Fried Chicken
Corp.**
P.O. Box 32070
Louisville, KY 40232
*Richard P. Mayer,
chairman and CEO*

Kercheval, Ken
P.O. Box 1350
Hollywood, CA 90078
Actor

Kerner, Fred
P.O. Box 952, Station B
Willowdale, ON. M2K 2T6
Canada
Book publisher, author

Kerr, Deborah
9255 Sunset Blvd., Suite 505
Los Angeles, CA 90069
Actress

Kerr, Walter I.
230 W. 41st St.
New York, NY 10036
Drama critic, author

Kerrigan, Thomas Anthony
Center for the Study of Man,
U. of Notre Dame
Notre Dame, IN 46556
Poet, editor, translator

Kerry, John Forbes
Office of Senate Members
Washington, DC 20510
U.S. senator

Kershner, Irvin
c/o Silverberg, Silverberg &
Knupp
1800 Century Park E.
Los Angeles, CA 90067
Motion picture director

Kesey, Ken
85829 Ridgeway Rd.
Pleasant Hill, OR 97455
Writer

Ketcham, Henry King
P.O. Box 800
Pebble Beach, CA 93953
*Cartoonist, creator of
"Dennis The Menace"*

Key, Donald
7519 N. Crossway Rd.
Milwaukee, WI 53217
Art critic

Key, Ted
1694 Glenhardie Rd.
Wayne, PA 19087
Cartoonist, creator of "Hazel"

Khan, Chaka
P.O. Box 1087
Pacific Palisades, CA 90272
Singer

Khomeini, Ayatollah Ruhollah
Qom, Iran
Ruler of Iran

Kidd, Michael
151 El Camino Dr.
Beverly Hills, CA 90212
Choreographer

Kidder, Margot
1888 Century Park E., Suite 1400
Los Angeles, CA 90067
Actress

Kidnis, Igor
20 Drummer Ln.
West Redding, CT 06896
Harpsichordist

Kiernan, Edward J.
412 1st St. SE.
Washington, DC 20003
Labor union official

Kilby, J. S.
7723 Midbury
Dallas, TX 75230
Inventor of the microchip

Kilday, George
1111 S. Broadway
Los Angeles, CA 90015
Columnist

Kiley, Richard Paul
c/o Stephen Draper
37 W. 57th St.
New York, NY 10019
Actor

Killebrew, Gwendolyn
165 W. 57th St.
New York, NY 10019
Opera singer

Kimberly-Clark Corp.
P.O. Box 619100
Dallas/Fort Worth Airport Station
Dallas, TX 75261
Darwin E. Smith,
chairman and CEO

Kimelman, Henry L.
P.O. Box 8240
St. Thomas, VI 00801
Ambassador

King, Alan
151 El Camino Dr.
Beverly Hills, CA 90212
Entertainer

King, B. B.
(Riley "Blues Boy" King)
c/o Sidney A. Seinberg
1414 Ave. of the Americas
New York, NY 10019
Blues guitarist

King, Bernard
New York Knickerbockers,
Madison Square Garden
4 Pennsylvania Plaza
New York, NY 10001
Basketball player

King, Billie Jean
c/o U.S. Tennis Association
51 E. 42nd St.
New York, NY 10017
Tennis player

King, Carole
c/o Free Flow Productions, Inc.
1209 Baylor St.
Austin, TX 78703
Composer, singer

King, Coretta Scott
(Mrs. Martin Luther
King, Jr.)
449 Auburn Ave. NE.
Atlanta, GA 30312
Lecturer, writer, concert singer

King, Larry L.
c/o Viking Press
40 W. 23rd St.
New York, NY 10010
Author, actor

King, Morgana
c/o Muse Records
160 W. 71st St.
New York, NY 10023
Jazz vocalist

King, Perry
c/o Pickwick, Meslansky,
Koenugsberg, Inc.
545 Madison Ave.
New York, NY 10022
Actor

King, Stephen
c/o Press Relations, Viking Press
625 Madison Ave.
New York, NY 10022
Novelist

Kingman, David Arthur
c/o Oakland A's, Oakland-
Alameda Coliseum
Oakland, CA 94621
Baseball player

Kingsley, Ben
c/o International Creative
Management
398/396 Oxford St.
London W1 England
Actor

Kinney Shoe Corp.
233 Broadway
New York, NY 10079
C. I. Anderson, president

Kinski, Klaus
Beta Strasse
8043 Unterfohring
Federal Republic of Germany
Actor

Kinski, Nastassja
c/o The Lantz Office, Inc.
888 Seventh Ave.
New York, NY 10106
Actress

Kirchschlager, Rudolph
Office of the President
Vienna, Austria
President of Austria

Kirkland, Gelsey
c/o Dube Zakin Management
1841 Broadway
New York, NY 10023
Ballet dancer

Kirkpatrick, Jeane
c/o American Enterprise Institute
1150 17th St.
NW. Washington, DC 20036
Political scientist

Kirkwood, Gene
10201 W. Pico Blvd.
Los Angeles, CA 90064
Motion picture producer

Kirkwood, James
1023 Catherine St.
Key West, FL 33040
Author, playwright, actor

Kiss
888 7th Ave.
New York, NY 10019
Rock group

Kissinger, Henry Alfred
c/o Kissinger Associates, Inc.
55 E. 52nd St.
New York, NY 10055
Former secretary of state

Kitt, Eartha Mae
c/o International Creative
Management
40 W. 57th S.
New York, NY 10019
Actress, singer

Kitty, Jerome T.
P.O. Box 1074
Weston, CT 06883
Playwright, stage director, actor

Klausen, Raymond
363 S. Las Palmas Ave.
Los Angeles, CA 90020
Television art director

Klein, Calvin Richard
205 W. 39th St.
New York, NY 10018
Designer

Klein, Norma
27 W. 96th St.
New York, NY 10025
Author

Klein, Robert
70 Middle Neck Rd., Suite 7
Great Neck, NY 11021
Actor, comedian

Klein, Ted
c/o Twilight Zone Magazine
800 2nd Ave.
New York, NY 10017
*Editor-in-chief, Twilight Zone
magazine*

Klemperer, Werner
9229 Sunset Blvd., Suite 201
Los Angeles, CA 90069
Actor

**Kliban, B. (Bernard Kli-
ban)**
c/o Workman Publishing Co., Inc.
One W. 39th St.
New York, NY 10018
Cartoonist

Kline, Kevin Delaney
c/o Triad Artists
888 7th Ave.
New York, NY 10019
Actor

Kline, Richard
9200 Sunset Blvd., Suite 414
Los Angeles, CA 90069
Comedian

Klotz, Florence
1050 Park Ave.
New York, NY 10028
Costume designer

Kluger, Richard
Back Brook Rd.
Ringoes, NJ 08551
Author, editor, critic

Klugman, Jack
9200 Sunset Blvd., Suite 909
Los Angeles, CA 91608
Actor

K-Mart Corp.
3100 W. Big Beaver
Troy, MI 48084
*Bernard M. Fauber,
chairman and CEO*

**Knauer, Virginia
Harrington**
U.S. Office of Consumer Affairs
Washington, DC 20201
Director

Knievel, Evel
9960 York Alpha Dr.
North Royalton, OH 44133
Daredevil

Knight, Gladys
c/o Network Talent International
Box 82, Suite 342A
98 Cuttermill Rd.
Great Neck, NY
Singer

Knight, James L.
c/o Knight-Ridder Newspaper,
Inc.
One Herald Plaza
Miami, FL 33132
Newspaperman

**Knight-Ridder Newspa-
pers, Inc.**
One Herald Plaza
Miami, FL 33101
*Alvah H. Chapman, Jr.,
chairman and CEO*

Knopf, Paul Mark
c/o Brown University, Div. of
Biology and Medicine
Providence, RI 02912
Immunoparasitologist

Knotts, Don
151 El Camino Dr.
Beverly Hills, CA 90212
Actor

Knowles, John
P.O. Box 939
Southampton, NY 11968
Author

Knowles, Tony
Municipality of Anchorage
P.O. Box 6650
Anchorage, AK 99502
Mayor of Anchorage

Knudsen Foods, Inc.
Box 2335, Terminal Annex
Los Angeles, CA 90051
*Dee R. Bangerter,
chairman and CEO*

Koch, Edward L.
Office of the Mayor, City Hall
New York, NY 10007
Mayor of New York City

Koch, Peter
1526 Willow Creek Rd.
Corvallis, MT 59828
Wood scientist

Konigsberg, Franklin Daniel
c/o Konigsberg Co.
10201 W. Pico Blvd.
Los Angeles, CA 90064
Motion picture and television producer

Konopka, Gisela Peiper
3809 Sheridan Ave. S.
Minneapolis, MN 55410
Educator, social worker, lecturer, author

Kool & the Gang
641 Lexington Ave., Suite 1450
New York, NY 10022
Pop music group

Kopit, Arthur
c/o International Creative Management
40 W. 57th St.
New York, NY 10019
Playwright

Koppel, Ted
c/o ABC News
1717 DeSales St. NW.
Washington, DC 20036
Anchorman, ABC News Nightline

Koppell, Bernie
151 El Camino Dr.
Beverly Hills, CA 90212
Actor

Korman, Harvey
c/o Singer & Lewak
10960 Wilshire Blvd.
Los Angeles, CA 90024
Actor, comedian

Kosar, Bernie
c/o Cleveland Browns, Municipal Stadium
Cleveland, OH 44114
Football player

Kosinski, Jerzy Nikodem
Hemisphere House 18-K
60 W. 57th St.
New York, NY 10019
Author

Kostelanetz, Richard
P.O. Box 73
Canal Street Station
New York, NY 10013
Writer, artist

Kotcheff, William Theodore
8899 Beverly Blvd.
Los Angeles, CA 90048
Director

Kotto, Yaphet
c/o The Artists Group Ltd.
1930 Century Park W., Suite 303
Los Angeles, CA 90067
Actor

Kraco Enterprises, Inc.
505 E. Euclid
Compton, CA 90224
Lawrence M. Kraines, president

Kraft, Inc.
Kraft Court
Glenview, IL 60025
John M. Richman,
chairman and CEO

Krainin, Julian
39 W. 55th St.
New York, NY 10019
Motion picture writer, producer,
and director, choreographer

Kramer, George M.
P.O. Box 45
Linden, NJ 07036
Chess player

Kramer, Stanley E.
P.O. Box 158
Bellevue, WA 98009
Motion picture director and
producer

Krantz, Judith Tarcher
c/o Krantz Productions
9601 Wilshire Blvd., Suite 343
Beverly Hills, CA 90210
Novelist

Krause, Bernard Leo
680 Beach St., Suite 414
San Francisco, CA 94109
Sonic artist, bio-acoustician,
composer, audioforensic scientist

Kreps, Juanita Morris
115 E. Duke Building
Duke University
Durham, NC 27706
Former secretary of commerce

Kreskin
201A N. Robertson Blvd.
Beverly Hills, CA 90211
Mentalist

Krieg, Dave
5303 Lake Washington Blvd.
Kirkland, WA 98033
Football player

Kristofferson, Kris
8899 Beverly Blvd.
Los Angeles, CA 90048
Singer, songwriter, actor

Krol, John
222 N. 17th St.
Philadelphia, PA 19103
Cardinal, Catholic Church

Kruger, Jerome
c/o National Bureau of Standards
Washington, DC 20234
Commerce Department official

Krupske, Danya
564 W. 52nd St.
New York, NY 10019
Director, choreographer

Kubek, Anthony Christopher
c/o NBC-TV
30 Rockefeller Plaza
New York, NY 10020
Sports announcer

Kubrick, Stanley
c/o Louis C. Blau, Loeb & Loeb
10100 Santa Monica Blvd.
Los Angeles, CA 90067
Motion picture producer, director, writer

Kuchinski, Mary Ann
Route 5, Box 200C
Danville, VA 24541
Knits wool caps for the stars

Kuhn, Bowie
15 W. 51st St.
New York, NY 10019
Former baseball commissioner

Kunin, Madeleine May
Office of Governor, Pavillion
Bldg., 5th Floor
Montpelier, VT 05602
Governor of Vermont

Kuralt, Charles Bishop
c/o CBS News
524 W. 57th St.
New York, NY 10019
Television news correspondent

Labelle, Patti
c/o Gallin-Morey & Associates
8730 Sunset Blvd., Penthouse W.
Los Angeles, CA 90069
Singer

Lach, Alma
710 N. Rush St.
Chicago, IL 60611
Author, food editor

Lachenbruch, Arthur Harold
345 Middlefield Rd.
Menlo Park, CA 94025
Research geophysicist

Lackenmier, James Richard
Kings College
133 N. River St.
Wilkes-Barre, PA 18702
Priest, college president

Lacy, Beatrice Cates
c/o Wright State University,
Fels Research Institute
800 Livermore St.
Yellow Springs, OH 45387
Psychophysiologist

Ladd, Alan Walbridge, Jr.
MGM/UA Entertainment Co.

10202 W. Washington Blvd.
Culver City, CA 90230
President, CEO of MGM/UA Entertainment

Ladd, Cheryl
151 El Camino Dr.
Beverly Hills, CA 90212
Actress

Laderman, Ezra
Box 689
Woods Hole, MA 02543
Composer, educator

L.A.D.I.E.S. (Life After Divorce Is Eventually Seeing)
P.O. Box 2974
Beverly Hills, CA 90213
Ex-wives of celebrities

Laffer, Arthur
1047 Galey Ave., Suite 402
Los Angeles, CA 90024
Economist

Lafferty, Perry Francis
c/o NBC Entertainment
3000 W. Alameda Blvd.
Burbank, CA 91505
Television exec.

LaFleur, Guy
c/o Montreal Canadiens
2313 Saint Catherine St. W.
Montreal PQ H3H 1N2
Canada
Hockey player

Lagasse, Leo D.
c/o UCLA Med. Center, Dept. of
Ob-Gyn
10833 Le Conte Ave.
Los Angeles, CA 90024
Gynecological onocologist

Lagerfeld, Karl Otto
Karl Lagerfeld Co.
144 Champs Elysees
Paris, France
Fashion designer

Lahr, John
c/o Alfred A. Knopf
201 E. 50th St.
New York, NY 10022
Author

**Laine, Cleo
(Clementina Dinah
Dankworth)**
c/o International Artists
Representation
235 Regent St.
London W1 England
Singer

Laird, Jack
c/o Universal Studios
Universal City, CA 91608
*Motion picture and television
writer, director, and producer*

LaLanne, Jack
P.O. Box 1249
Burbank, CA 91507-1249
Fitness expert

Lamas, Lorenzo
c/o Charter Management
9000 Sunset Blvd.
Los Angeles, CA 90069
Actor, race car driver

Lamb, Lawrence Edward
135 Downing Dr.
San Antonio, TX 78209
Cardiologist

Lambert, Jack
c/o Pittsburgh Steelers
300 Stadium Circle
Pittsburgh, PA 15212
Former football player

Lambeth, Victor Neal
U. of Missouri Dept. of Horticul-
ture
Columbia, MO 65201
Horticulturist, researcher

**Lambremont, Edward
Nelson**
c/o Nuclear Science Center
Louisiana State University
Baton Rouge, LA 70803
Nuclear science educator

Lamm, Richard Douglas
State Capitol, Room 136
Denver, CO 80203-1792
Governor of Colorado

Lammel, Jeanette Osborn
258 Viewmont Ave.
Vallejo, CA 94590
Interior designer

Lamont, Corliss
315 W. 106th St.
New York, NY 10025
Philosophy educator, author

**Lancaster, Burt
(Burton Stephen Lancaster)**
P.O. Box 67838
Los Angeles, CA 90067
Actor

Lance, Bert
P.O. Box 637
Calhoun, GA 30701
*Former government official,
banker*

Landau, Jacob
c/o Pratt Institute
Brooklyn, NY 11205
Artist

Landau, Martin
c/o Harry Gold & Associates
8285 Sunset Blvd., Suite One
Los Angeles, CA 90046
Actor

**Landers, Ann
(Mrs. Esther P. Lederer)**
c/o Chicago Sun Times
401 N. Wabash Ave.
Chicago, IL 60611
Columnist

Landesberg, Steve
151 El Camino Dr.
Beverly Hills, CA 90212
Actor

Landis, John David
1888 Century Park E., Suite 1400
Los Angeles, CA 90667
*Motion picture writer and
director*

Land O'Lakes, Inc.
4001 Lexington Ave. N.
Arden Hills, MN 55126
*Ralph Hofstad,
president and CEO*

**Landon, Michael
(Eugene Maurice Orowitz)**
10351 Santa Monica
Blvd., Number 402
Los Angeles, CA 90025
Actor

Landrieu, Moon
4301 S. Prieur St.
New Orleans, LA 70125
Former secretary of HUD, lawyer

Landry, Tom
c/o Dallas Cowboys
6116 N. Central Expressway
Dallas, TX 75206
Football coach

Lang, Jennings
100 Universal City Plaza
Universal City, CA 91608
Producer

Lang, Pearl
c/o American Dance Center
1515 Broadway
New York, NY 10036
Dancer, choreographer

Langdon, Sue Ane
c/o Lew Sherrell Agency Ltd.
7060 Hollywood Blvd.
Los Angeles, CA 90028
Actress

Lange, Jessica
8899 Beverly Blvd.
Los Angeles, CA 90048
Actress

Lange, Ted
The Artists Group Ltd.
1930 Century Park W., Suite 303
Los Angeles, CA 90067
Actor, director

Langella, Frank
8899 Beverly Blvd.
Los Angeles, CA 90048
Actor

Langfield, Joanna
c/o WABC
1330 Ave. of the Americas
New York, NY 10019
Radio talk show host

Lansbury, Angela
151 El Camino Dr.

Beverly Hills, CA 90212
Actress

Lansing, Robert Howell
c/o Phil Gersh Agency
222 N. Canon Dr.
Beverly Hills, CA 90210
Actor, director

Lantz, Walter
6311 Romaine St.
Hollywood, CA 90038
Cartoonist, creator of "Woody Woodpecker"

Lanyon, Wesley E.
c/o American Museum of Natural History
New York, NY 10024
Ornithologist, museum curator

Lardner, Ring Wilmer, Jr.
c/o Russell & Volkening Inc.
551 5th Ave.
New York, NY 10017
Author

Laredo, Ruth
c/o Gurtman & Murtha Associates
162 W. 56th St.
New York, NY 10019
Concert pianist

Larroquette, John Bernard
8730 Sunset Blvd., 6th Floor
Los Angeles, CA 90067
Actor

Larson, Dale M.
c/o Amex Life Assurance Co.
1650 Los Gemos Dr.
San Rafael, CA 94903-1899
*Author, expert in long-term care
insurance*

Larson, Glen
P.O. Box 900
Los Angeles, CA 90213
Television producer, writer

Lasarow, William Julius
c/o U.S. Bankruptcy Court
930 U.S. Courthouse,
312 N. Spring St.
Los Angeles, CA 90012
Chief bankruptcy judge

Lasorda, Tom Charles
1000 Elysian Park Ave.
Los Angeles, CA 90012
*Manager, Los Angeles Dodgers
baseball team*

Lasser, Louise
9120 Sunset Blvd., Suite A
Los Angeles, CA 90069
Actress

Lasswell, Fred
c/o King Features Syndicate
235 E. 45th St.
New York, NY 10017
Cartoonist

Lattanzi, Matt
8485 Melrose Blvd.
Los Angeles, CA 90069
Actor

Lauder, Estee
767 5th Ave.
New York, NY 10022
Cosmetics company exec.

Lauper, Cyndi
c/o David Wolff Productions, Inc.
853 7th Ave., Suite 9D
New York, NY 10019
Pop singer

Laura Scudder's, Inc.
1525 N. Raymond Ave.
Anaheim, CA 92801
Joseph W. Halligan, president

**Lauren, Ralph
(Ralph Lifschitz)**
40 W. 55th St.
New York, NY 10019
Fashion designer

Lautenberg, Frank R.
Hart Senate Office Bldg.
Room 717
Washington, DC 20510
U.S. senator

Laventhol, Henry
Rural Delivery One
Box 44, Hanover St.
Yorktown Heights, NY 10598
Painter, etcher

Laver, Rodney George
P.O. Box 4798
Hilton Head Island, NC 29928
Tennis player

Lavin, Linda
8500 Wilshire Blvd., Suite 506
Beverly Hills, CA 90211
Actress

Law, John Philip
8899 Beverly Blvd.
Los Angeles, CA 90048
Actor

Lawrence, Pelham Bissell
P.O. Box 1537
Salisbury, MD 21801
Poultry exec.

Lawrence, Steve
c/o Lipsman & Associates
8961 Sunset Blvd.
Los Angeles, CA 90069
Entertainer

Lawrence, Vicki Ann
c/o Lawrence/Shultz Inc.
3350 Barham Blvd.
Los Angeles, CA 90068
Singer, dancer, actress

Lawson, Dr. Richard
920 S. Roberton Blvd., Number 2
Los Angeles, CA 90035
Psychologist

Lawson, William David III
Box 638
Gastonia, NC 28052
Cotton merchant

Laxalt, Paul
Russell Senate Office Bldg.,
Room 323A
Washington, DC 20510
U.S. senator

Layton, Joe
c/o Roy Gerber Associates
9200 Sunset Blvd., Suite 620
Los Angeles, CA 90069
Director, choreographer

Lazarus, Mel
1703 Kaiser Ave.
Irvine, CA 92714
Cartoonist, creator of "Momma"

LA-Z-Boy Chair Co.
1284 N. Telegraph Rd.
Monroe, MI 48161
E. M. Knabusch, chairman

Lea, Charles Lewis, Jr.
c/o Dillon Read & Co., Inc.
46 William St.
New York, NY 10005
Venture capitalist

Leach, Robin
c/o Television Programing Enterprises
1014 N. Sycamore
Los Angeles, CA 90038
Host, Lifestyles of the Rich and Famous

Leachman, Cloris
c/o McCartt, Oreck, Barrett
9200 Sunset Blvd., Suite 1009
Los Angeles, CA 90069
Actress

Leahy, Patrick Joseph
Russell Senate Office Bldg.
Room 433
Washington, DC 20510
U.S. senator

Lean, David
c/o Columbia Pictures International
711 5th Ave.
New York, NY 10022
Motion picture director

Lear, Norman
c/o Act III Communications
1800 Century Park E.
Los Angeles, CA 90067
Motion picture and television writer, producer, director

Learned, Michael
c/o Henderson/Hogan Agency Inc.
247 S. Beverly Dr.
Beverly Hills, CA 90210
Actress

Leary, Lewis
128 Carol Woods
Chapel Hill, NC 27514
Writer, lecturer

Leary, Timothy
P.O. Box 69886
Los Angeles, CA 90069
Psychologist, author

Le Carre, John (David John Moore Cornwell)
c/o John Farquharson Ltd.
162-168 Regent St.
London W1R 5TB England
Author

Lee, Brenda
2126 N. North St.
Peoria, IL 61604
Singer

Lee, Christopher
245 W. 104th St.
New York, NY 10025
Actor

Lee, Joanna
c/o Christiana Productions
532 Colorado Ave., Suite 202
Santa Monica, CA 90401
Television writer, director, producer

The Peggy Lee Fan Club
744 Collier Dr.
San Leandro, CA 94577
Robert Stromm, president

Lee, Robert Edwin
15725 Royal Oak Rd.
Encino, CA 91436
Playwright

The Lee Apparel Co., Inc.
9001 W. 67th St.
Merriam, KS 66202
M. G. Winne, president

Lefferts, George
Robbins Rest
Fire Island, NY 11776
Writer, producer, director

Leftwich, James Adolf
P.O. Box 3333
La Jolla, CA 92037
Former boxer, writer, publisher, PR exec.

L'Eggs Products, Inc.
P.O. Box 2495
Winston Salem, NC 27102
Walter Pilher, president

Lehman, Christopher M.
National Security Council
Washington, DC 20500
Special assistant to the president

Lehman, Earnest
8955 Beverly Blvd.
Los Angeles, CA 90048
Author, motion picture writer, producer, director

Leibman, Ron
8899 Beverly Blvd.
Los Angeles, CA 90048
Actor

Leiferman, Silvia Weiner
10155 Collins Ave.
Bal Harbour, FL 33154
Artist, civic worker

**Leigh, Janet
(Jaanette Helen Morrison)**
c/o Fred Amsel & Associates
291 S. La Cienega Blvd., Suite 307
Beverly Hills, CA 90211
Actress

Lemmon, Jack
c/o Jalem Productions
141 El Camino Dr.
Beverly Hills, CA 90212
Actor

Lemon, Meadowlark
30 Rockefeller Plaza
New York, NY 10020
Basketball player, member of Harlem Globetrotters

Lendl, Ivan
c/o U.S. Tennis Association
51 E. 42nd St.
New York, NY 10017
Pro tennis player

Lennon, Julian
P.O. Box 1060
Lenox Hill Station
New York, NY 10021
Singer, songwriter, musician

Lenz, Kay
c/o Gage Group, Inc.
9229 Sunset Blvd., Suite 306
Los Angeles, CA 90069
Actress

Leon, Tania Justina
211 W. 56th St., Suite 18M
New York, NY 10019
Pianist, composer

Leonard, Sheldon
c/o Sheldon Leonard Productions
315 S. Beverly Dr.
Beverly Hills, CA 90212
Television producer, director

**Leonard, Sugar Ray
(Ray Charles Leonard)**
c/o Home Box Office
Time Bldg., Rockefeller Center
New York, NY 10020
*Boxer, world middle-weight
champion*

Lerner, Louis Abraham
7519 N. Ashland Ave.
Chicago, IL 60626
*Former ambassador, newspaper
publisher*

Leroy, Edward Carwile
171 Ashley Ave.
Charleston, SC 29403
Rheumatologist

Letterman, David
151 El Camino Dr.

Beverly Hills, CA 90212
Comedian, writer, host of Late
Night

Level 42
c/o International Creative
Management
40 W. 57th St.
New York, NY 10019
Pop music group

Leventhal, Harold
250 W. 57th St.
New York, NY 10019
Talent manager, producer

Levey, Robert Frank
c/o Washington Post
1150 15th St.
Washington, DC 20071
Columnist

Levin, Carl
Russell Senate Office Bldg.
Room 459
Washington, DC 20510
U.S. senator

Levin, Ira
c/o Harold Ober & Associates
40 E. 49th St.
New York, NY 10017
Author, playwright

Levin, Jack
220 Huntington Plaza
Northeastern University
Boston, MA 02115

Professor of sociology, expert in the history of gossip

Levine, Michael
8730 Sunset Blvd., 6th Floor
Los Angeles, CA 90069
Author, The Address Book

Levine, Philip
c/o Ortho Research Foundation
Raritan, NJ 08869
Immunohematologist, biomedical scientist, geneticist

Levi Strauss & Co.
1155 Battery St.
San Francisco, CA 94111
Robert D. Haas, president and CEO

Levitz Furniture Corp.
1317 NW. 167th St.
Miami, FL 33169
Robert M. Elliot, chairman and CEO

Levy, Louis
12317 Ridge Circle
Los Angeles, CA 90049
Chess master

Lewis, Ann Frank
c/o Democratic National Committee
1625 Massachusetts Ave. NW.
Washington, DC 20036
Political activist

Lewis, Geoffrey
151 El Camino Dr.
Beverly Hills, CA 90212
Actor

Lewis, Huey, and The News
P.O. Box 819
Mill Valley, CA 94942
Rock and roll band

Lewis, Jerry
c/o Muscular Dystrophy Association
810 7th Ave.
New York, NY 10019
Comedian, actor

Lewis, Jerry Lee
c/o MCA Records Inc.
70 Universal City Plaza
Universal City, CA 91608
Rock performer

Lewis, Shari
c/o Management III
9744 Wilshire Blvd.
Beverly Hills, CA 90212
Ventriloquist, puppeteer

Lewy, John Edwin
1430 Tulane Ave.
New Orleans, LA 70119
Pediatric nephrologist

Li, Choh Hao
901 Arlington Ave.
Berkeley, CA 94707
Biochemist, endocrinologist

Library of Congress
10 First St. SE.
Washington, DC 20540
Daniel J. Boorstin

Lightfoot, Gordon
c/o International Creative
Management
40 W. 57th St.
New York, NY 10019
Singer, songwriter

Lightstone, Marilyn
c/o Moses Znaimer
99 Queen St.
East Toronto, ON M5C
Canada
Actress

The Limited, Inc.
2 Limited Parkway
Columbus, OH 43230
Leslie H. Wexner, chairman

Linden, Hal
c/o William Morris Agency
1350 Ave. of the Americas
New York, NY 10019
Actor

Link, Mae Mills
c/o Kroontz Center For Advanced Studies
Riverton, VA 22651
*Space medicine historian and
consultant*

**Linkletter, Art
(Arthur Gordon Linkletter)**
8500 Wilshire Blvd.
Beverly Hills, CA 90211
Radio, television broadcaster

Linn, Edward Allen
46 Marilyn Blvd.
Plainview, NY 11803
Writer

Liotta, Ray
12207 Riverside Dr.
Number 207
North Hollywood, CA 91607
Actor

**Lipton, Inc.
(Thomas J. Lipton, Inc.)**
800 Sylvan Ave.
Englewood Cliffs, NJ 07632
*H. M. Tibbetts,
president and CEO*

Lithgow, John Arthur
1888 Century Park E., Suite 1400
Los Angeles, CA 90067
Actor

Little, Cleavon
c/o Jack Fields Agency
9255 Sunset Blvd.
Los Angeles, CA 90069
Actor

Little, Elbert Luther, Jr.
Smithsonian Institute Department
of Botany
Washington, DC 20560
Dendrologist, botanist

Little, Rich
c/o Triad Artists, Inc.
10100 Santa Monica Blvd.
16th Floor
Los Angeles, CA 90067
Impressionist, actor

Livingston, Myra Cohn
9308 Readcrest Dr.
Beverly Hills, CA 90210
Writer, poet, educator

LL Cool J
c/o Rush Productions
298 Elizabeth St.
New York, NY 10012
Rapper

Lloyd, Christopher
c/o Phil Gersh Agency, Inc.
222 N. Canon Dr.
Beverly Hills, CA 90210
Actor

Lloyd, Michael Jeffrey
10960 Wilshire Blvd., Suite 826
Los Angeles, CA 90024
Record producer, motion picture producer

Locke, Sondra
151 El Camino Dr.
Beverly Hills, CA 90212
Actress

Lockheed Corp.
2555 Hollywood Way
Burbank, CA 91520
Lawrence O. Kitchen, chairman and CEO

Locklear, Heather
P.O. Box 124
Los Angeles, CA 90068
Actress

Lockwood, Gary
9000 Sunset Blvd., Suite 315
Los Angeles, CA 90069
Actor

Lodge, Henry Cabot
275 Hale St.
Beverly, MA 01915
Former senator, former government official, author

Lodge, John Davis
U.S. Embassy
Jubliaeumstrasse
93 Bern, Switzerland 3005
Ambassador, lawyer, former congressman, governor, actor

Lofton, James David
c/o Green Bay Packers
1265 Lombardi Ave.
Green Bay, WI 54304
Football player

Loggins, Kenny
10100 Santa Monica Blvd.
16th Floor
Los Angeles, CA 90067
Singer, songwriter

London, Dorothy
9200 Sunset Blvd., Suite 1099
Los Angeles, CA 90069
Actress

Long, Russell
U.S. Senate
Washington, DC 20510
U.S. senator

Long, Shelly
151 El Camino Dr.
Beverly Hills, CA 90212
Actress

Longs Drug Stores Corp.
141 N. Civic Dr.
Walnut Creek, CA 94596
J. M. Long, chairman

Loomis Corp.
55 Battery St.
Seattle, WA 98121
Charles W. Loomis,
chairman of the board

Lopez, Jose Portillo
Palacio Nacional Mexico
DF Mexico
Former president of Mexico

Lopez, Nancy
One Erieview Plaza
Cleveland, OH 44114
Golfer

Lopez, Priscilla
c/o William Morris Agency
1350 Ave. of the Americas
New York, NY 10019
Actress

Lorber, Jeff
c/o Left Bank Management
2519 Carmen Crest
Hollywood, CA 90068
Recording artist

Lord, Jack
c/o Lord & Lady Enterprises, Inc.
4999 Kahala Ave.
Honolulu, HI 96816
Actor, director, artist, producer

Loren, Sophia
6 Rue Charles Bonnet
Geneva, Switzerland
Actress

Loring, Gloria
c/o Ryder Public Relations
9348 Civic Center, Suite 407
Beverly Hills, CA 90210
Actress, singer

Los Lobos
P.O. Box 1304
Burbank, CA 91507
Rock band

Lott, Ronnie
711 Nevada St.
Redwood City, CA 94061
Football player

Louganis, Greg E.
P.O. Box 4068
Malibu, CA 90265
Olympic athlete

Lougheed, Peter
307 Legislature Bldg.
Edmonton, AB T5K 2B7
Canada
Premier of Alberta

Loverboy
1888 Century Park E., Suite 1400
Los Angeles, CA 90067
Pop music band

Lowe, Rob
8899 Beverly Blvd.
Los Angeles, CA 90048
Actor

Lowy, Jay Stanton
Jobete Music Co., Inc.
6255 Sunset Blvd.
Los Angeles, CA 90028
Music Publisher

Loy, Myrna
222 S. Orange Dr.
Los Angeles, CA 90036
Actress

The Loyal Order of Moose
Mooseheart, IL 60539
Donald H. Ross, supreme secretary

Lucas, George
P.O. Box 2009
San Rafael, CA 94912
Motion picture writer, producer, director

Lucci, Susan
c/o ABC Press Dept.
1330 Ave. of the Americas
New York, NY 10019
Actress

Luce, Henry, III
720 5th Ave.
New York, NY 10019
Foundation exec.

Lucky Stores, Inc.
6300 Clark Ave.
Dublin, CA 94568
John M. Lillie, president

Lugar, Richard
Hart Senate Office Bldg.
Room 306
Washington, DC 20510
U.S. senator

Luken, Charles
Office of the Mayor, City Hall
Cincinnati, OH 45202
Mayor of Cincinnati

Lumet, Sidney
c/o LAH Film Corp.
1775 Broadway
New York, NY 10019
Motion picture director

Lumm, Herman Tsui Fai
P.O. Box 2560
Honolulu, HI 96804
Chief justice of Hawaiian Supreme Court

Lunden, Joan
c/o ABC News Dept.
1330 Ave. of the Americas
New York, NY 10019
Co-host; Good Morning America

Lynch, William Dennis, Jr.
c/o CBS News
2020 M St. NW.
Washington, DC 20036
Broadcast journalist

Lynley, Carol Ann
c/o Paul Kohner
9169 Sunset Blvd.
Los Angeles, CA 90069
Actress

Lynn, Frederick Michael
801 Inverness Dr.
Rancho Mirage, CA 92270
Baseball player

Lynn, Janet
4215 Marsh Ave.
Rockford, IL 61111
Figure skater

Lynn, Loretta Web
P.O. Box 23470
Nashville, TN 37202
Country western singer

Lynne, Jeff
c/o Jet Promotions, Inc.
2099 Century Park E., Suite 414
Los Angeles, CA 90067
*Music producer, leader of the
Electric Light Orchestra*

MacArthur, James
Korman Contemporary Artists
132 Lasky Dr.
Beverly Hills, CA 90212
Actor

MacDonald, Joseph Albert Freil
c/o McInnes Cooper & Robertson
1673 Bedford Row
Halifax NS B3J 2V1
Canada
Barrister, solicitor

MacGraw, Ali
8899 Beverly Blvd.
Los Angeles, CA 90048
Actress

Macinnes, Helen
15 Jeffrey Ln.
East Hampton, NY 11937
Author

Mackie, Bob
c/o Bob Mackie Originals
550 7th Ave., 22nd Floor
New York, NY 10018
Costume and fashion designer

Mack Trucks, Inc.
2100 Mack Blvd.
Allentown, PA 18103
J. B. Curcio, president and CEO

Maclaine, Shirley
c/o Chasin-Park-Citron Agency
9255 Sunset Blvd.
Los Angeles, CA 90069
Actress, author

Maclean, Alistair
c/o William Collins & Son Co. Ltd.
8 Grafton St.
London SC W1 England
Author

Macleod, Gavin
151 El Camino Dr.
Beverly Hills, CA 90212
Actor

MacMurray, Fred
8899 Beverly Blvd.
Los Angeles, CA 90048
Actor

MacNamara, Donald Eoin Joseph
444 W. 56th St.
New York, NY 10019
Criminologist

Macnee, Patrick (Daniel Patrick Macnee)
c/o Phil Gersh Agency, Inc.
222 N. Canon Dr.
Beverly Hills, CA 90210
Actor

Macneil, Robert (Robert Breckenridge Ware Macneil)
c/o WNET 13
356 W. 58th St.
New York, NY 10019
Broadcast journalist

MacRae, Gordon
151 El Camino Dr.
Beverly Hills, CA 90212
Singer, actor

MacRae, Sheila Stephens
c/o Talent Management-
International
91.10 Sunset Blvd.
Los Angeles, CA 90069
Entertainer

Macy's (R.H. Macy & Co., Inc.)
151 W. 34th St.
New York, NY 10001
*Edward S. Finkelstein,
chairman and CEO*

Madden, John
c/o CBS Sports
51 W. 52nd St.
New York, NY 10019
Television sports commentator

Madlock, William, Jr.
c/o Los Angeles Dodgers
Dodger Stadium
1000 Elysian Park Ave.
Los Angeles, CA 90012
Baseball player

Madonna
c/o Demann Entertainment
9200 Sunset Blvd., Suite 915
Los Angeles, CA 90069
Singer

Madrid Hurtado, Miguel de la
Presidencia de la Republica
Palacio Nacional
Mexico City, Mexico 06220
President of Mexico

Magic Chef, Inc.
740 King Edward Ave.
Cleveland, TN 37311
*S. B. Rymer, Jr., chairman and
CEO*

Mahaffey, John
3100 Richmond Ave., Suite 500
Houston, TX 77098
Pro golfer

Mahal, Taj (Henry St. Claire Fredericks)
c/o Folklore Productions
1671 Appian Way
Santa Monica, CA 90401
Musician, composer

Mahler, Donald
c/o Metropolitan Opera
Lincoln Center
New York, NY 10023
Ballet master

Mahoney, J. Daniel
51 W. 51st St.
New York, NY 10019
*Chairman of New York State
Conservative party*

Mahre, Phil
P.O. Box 100
Park City, UT 84060
Alpine ski racer

**Maier, Leonard Cheney,
Jr.**
City Hall
Milwaukee, WI 53202
Mayor of Milwaukee

Mailer, Norman
c/o Rembar
19 W. 44th St.
New York, NY 10036
Author

Majors, Lee
c/o Management 3
4570 Encino Ave.
Encino, CA 91316
Actor

Makos, Christopher
200 W. 15th St.
New York, NY 10011
Photographer

**Malden, Karl
(Malden Sekulovich)**
151 El Camino Dr.
Beverly Hills, CA 90212
Actor

Malina, Judith
c/o ML Beck
800 West End Ave.
New York, NY 10025
*Theatrical exec., actress,
writer, director*

Malkovich, John
c/o Steppenwolf Theatre
2851 N. Halstead St.
Chicago, IL 60657
Actor

Malmsteen, Yngwie
c/o International Creative
Management
40 W. 57th St.
New York, NY 10019
Rock guitarist

Malone, Moses
c/o Philadelphia 76ers
Vets Stadium
P.O. Box 25040
Philadelphia, PA 19147
Basketball player

Malt-O-Meal Co.
2601 IDS Tower
Minneapolis, MN 55402
Glenn S. Brooks, president

Manchester, Melissa
c/o Lippman-Kahane
9669 Oak Pass Rd.
Beverly Hills, CA 90210
Singer, songwriter

Mancini, Henry
c/o Regency Artists Ltd.
9200 Sunset Blvd., Suite 823
Los Angeles, CA 90069
Composer

Mancini, Ray (Boom Boom)
750 Bundy Dr., Number 108
Los Angeles, CA 90049
Boxer

Mancuso, Nick
409 N. Camden Dr., Suite 202
Beverly Hills, CA 90210
Actor, director

Mandlikova, Hana
Vymolova 8
Praha 5
150 00 Czechoslovakia
Tennis player

Mandrell, Barbara
c/o World Class Talent
1522 Demonbreeux
Nashville, TN 27203
Country singer

Manhattan Transfer
Box 1842, Number 373
Encino, CA 91426
Singing group

Manilow, Barry
c/o International Creative
Management
40 W. 57th St.
New York, NY 10019
Singer, composer

Mankiller, Wilma P.
P.O. Box 948
Tahlequah, OK 74465
Chief of the Cherokee Nation

Mann, Delbert
c/o Caroline Productions, Inc.
401 S. Burnside Ave.
Los Angeles, CA 90036
Motion picture, television and theater director and producer

Mann, Herbie
c/o Atlantic Records
75 Rockefeller Plaza
New York, NY 10020
Flutist

Manoff, Dinah Beth
165 W. 46th St., Suite 914
New York, NY 10036
Actress

Manson, Charles
California Medical Facility
Vacaville, CA 95688
Convicted mass murderer

Mantle, Mickey Charles
8080 Central St., Suite 900
Dallas, TX 75206
Athlete, marketing consultant

Manufacturers Hanover Corp.
270 Park Ave.
New York, NY 10017
John F. McGillicuddy, chairman and CEO

Marantz Co., Inc.
20525 Nordhoff St.
Chatsworth, CA 91311
Joseph S. Tushinsky,
chairman and CEO

Marceau, Marcel
c/o Ecole De Mimodrame De
Paris Marcel Marceau
17 Rue Rene Boulanger
Paris 75010 France
Mime, actor, director, painter

March of Dimes Birth
Defects Foundation
1275 Mamaroneck Ave.
White Plains, NY 10605
Charles L. Massey

Marchand, Nancy
c/o William Morris Agency
1350 Ave. of the Americas
New York, NY 10019
Actress

Marchese, Steve
1545 Newport Blvd.
Costa Mesa, CA 92629
President, Steve's Detailing. Uses
cotton swabs, tooth brushes and
popsicle sticks for special cleaning
of cars

Margo, Phil
1328 N. Gower, 5th Floor
Los Angeles, CA 90028
Theatrical producer

Margolin, Stuart
c/o Kohner-Levy Agency
9169 Sunset Blvd.
Los Angeles, CA 90069
Actor

Marin, Cheech
(Richard Anthony Marin)
c/o Press Relations, Columbia
Pictures
Colgems Square
Burbank, CA 91505
Writer, actor, comedian

Marino, Dan
c/o Miami Dolphins
3550 Biscayne Blvd.
Miami, FL 33157
Football player

Marks, Johnny
1619 Broadway
New York, NY 10019
Songwriter

Marks, Meyer Benjamin
333 Arthur Godfrey Rd.
Miami Beach, FL 33140
Pediatric allergist

Marlowe, George M.
14003 Palaway Way, Suite 310
Marina Del Rey, CA 90292
President, Video Pitch, a company
that puts together business pitches
on video for advertising agencies

Marr, David Francis
15835 Park Ten Place, Suite 103
Houston, TX 77084
Golfer, television announcer, golf course architect

Marriott Corp.
Marriott Dr.
Washington, DC 20058
J. W. Marriott, Jr., chairman

Marsalis, Wynton
c/o Agency for the Performing Arts, Inc.
9000 Sunset Blvd., Suite 1200
Los Angeles, CA 90069
Musician

Marsh, John O., Jr.
Office of the Secretary
of the Army
The Pentagon
Washington, DC 20310
Secretary of the army

Marshall, E. G.
c/o William Morris Agency
1350 Ave. of the Americas
New York, NY 10019
Actor

Marshall, Gary
c/o Paramount TV Productions
5451 Marathon St.
Los Angeles, CA 90038
Television writer, producer, director

**Marshall, Penny
(C. Penny Marshall)**
1888 Century Park E., Suite 1400
Los Angeles, CA 90067
Actress

Marshall, Thurgood
Supreme Court of the United States
Washington, DC 20543
Associate Justice, U.S. Supreme Court

Marshalls, Inc.
30 Harvard Mill Square
P.O. Box 1000-34
Wakefield, MA 01880
Francis C. Rooney, Jr., chairman

Martens, Wilfred
Office of the Premier
Brussels, Belgium
Premier of Belgium

**Martin, Billy
(Alfred Manuel Martin)**
New York Yankees, Yankee Stadium
Bronx, NY 10451
Former manager, New York Yankees

Martin, Dean
c/o Agency for the Performing Arts, Inc.
9000 Sunset Blvd., Suite 1200
Los Angeles, CA 90069
Singer, actor

Martin, Don
P.O. Box 1330
South Miami, FL 33234
Cartoonist

Martin, Kiel
c/o Freeman & Sutton Public
Relations
8961 Sunset Blvd., 2nd Floor
Los Angeles, CA 90069
Actor

Martin, Mary
c/o Richard Grant
1480 N. Doheny Dr.
Los Angeles, CA 90069
Actress, singer

Martin, Steve
7858 Beverly Blvd.
Los Angeles, CA 90036
Actor, comedian

Marvel Comic Group
387 Park Ave. S.
New York, NY 10016
James E. Galton, chairman

Marx, Arthur (Julius Marx)
c/o Scott Meredith
845 3rd Ave.
New York, NY 10022
*Son of Groucho Marx, author,
playwright*

Marx, Richard
c/o Left Bank Management
2519 Carmen Crest
Hollywood, CA 90068
Pop singer, songwriter, musician

Mary Kay Cosmetics, Inc.
8787 Stemmons Freeway
Dallas, TX 75247
Mary Kay Ash, chairman

Maserati Automobiles, Inc.
1501 Caton Ave.
Baltimore, MD 21227
George A. Garbutt, president

Mason, Marsha
c/o Nei-Son Associates
150 El Camino Dr., Suite 207
Beverly Hills, CA 90212
Actress

Mason, Pamela Helen
1018 Pamela Dr.
Beverly Hills, CA 90210
Actress, producer, writer

Mastroianni, Marcello
Via di Porta
San Sebastiano 15
Rome 00179 Italy
Actor

**Mathias, Charles
McCurdy, Jr.**
United States Senate
Washington, DC 20510
U.S. senator

Mathis, Johnny
c/o Rojon Productions
3500 W. Olive Ave.
Number 750
Burbank, CA 91505
Singer

Matrix One
6310 S. San Vicente Blvd.
Los Angeles, CA 90048
Fitness club of the stars

Matsunaga, Spark Masayuki
Hart Senate Office Bldg.
Room 109
Washington, DC 20510
U.S. senator

Matsushima, Satoshi
525 Davey Lab
University Park, PA 16802
Astronomer, educator

Mattel, Inc.
5150 Rosecrans Ave.
Hawthorne, CA 90250
Thomas J. Kalinske, president

Matthau, Walter
10100 Santa Monica Blvd.
Suite 2200
Los Angeles, CA 90067
Actor

Mattingly, Mack F.
Hart Senate Office Bldg.
Room 320
Washington, DC 20510
U.S. senator

Maurice, Dick
c/o Las Vegas Sun
121 S. Highland Dr.
Las Vegas, NV 89106
Syndicated writer, television host

Mawardi, Osman Kamel
10900 Euclid Ave.
Cleveland, OH 44106
Plasma physicist

Max Factor & Co.
700 Fairfield Ave.
Stamford, CT 06904
Paul Masturgo, president

May, Elaine
c/o Actor's Equity
165 W. 46th St.
New York, NY 10036
Entertainer, director

Mayall, John
Box 210103
San Francisco, CA 94188
Blues musician

Mayer, Jean
c/o Tufts University
Medford, MA 02155
President of Tufts University, scientist

Mayfield, Curtis Lee
Box 724677
Atlanta, GA 30339
Musician, songwriter

Mays, Willie
Bally's Park Place
Broadway and Park Place
Atlantic City, NJ 08401
Baseball player

Maytag Corp.
403 W. 4th St. N.
Newton, IA 50108
D. J. Krumm, president and CEO

Mazursky, Paul
8899 Beverly Blvd.
Los Angeles, CA 90048
Motion picture writer, producer

MCA, Inc.
100 Universal City Plaza
Universal City, CA 91608
*Lew R. Wasserman,
chairman and CEO*

McAdoo, Bob
P.O. Box 25040
Philadelphia, PA 19147-0240
Basketball player

McCallum, David
c/o Don Buchwald & Associates
10 E. 44th St.
New York, NY 10017
Actor

McCarthy, Eugene
c/o EPM Publications, Inc.
1003 Turkey Run Rd.
McLean, VA 22101
Writer, former senator

**McCartney, Paul
(James Paul McCartney)**
c/o MPL Communications
One Soho Sq.
London W1V 6BQ England
Musician, songwriter

McCheese, Mayor
One McDonald Plaza
Oak Brook, IL 60521
*Mayor of McDonaldland, fast food
spokesburger*

**McClanahan, Rue
(Eddi-Rue McClanahan)**
899 Beverly Blvd.
Los Angeles, CA 90048
Actress

**McClendon, Ernestine
Epps**
6615 Franklin Ave., Suite 302
Los Angeles, CA 90028
*Drama coach, actress,
writer, producer*

McClure, James A.
Dirksen Senate Office Bldg.
Room 361
Washington, DC 20510
U.S. senator

**McConnell, Addison
Mitchell, Jr.**
Russell Senate Office Bldg.,
Room 120
Washington, DC 20510
U.S. senator

**McCormack, Richard
Thomas Fox**
c/o U.S. State Department
2201 C St., Room 6959
NW. Washington, DC 20501
*U.S. ambassador to Organization
of American States*

McCormick, Hope Baldwin
1530 N. State Pkwy.
Chicago, IL 60610
Former member of Republican National Committee

McCovey, Willie
Candlestick Park
San Francisco, CA 94124
Baseball player

McCraney, Gerald
c/o Michael Karg
247 S. Beverly Dr.
Beverly Hills, CA 90212
Actor

McCune, Emmett Lee
Route One, Box 107B
Hallsville, MO 65255
Avian pathologist

McDaniel, Dolan Kenneth
7800 Banner Dr.
Dallas, TX 75251
Seismic exploration company exec.

McDonald, Michael
c/o Frontline Management
80 Universal City Plaza
Universal City, CA 91608
Singer, songwriter, musician

McDonald, Ronald
One McDonald Plaza
Oak Brook, IL 60521
Spokesclown

McDonald's Corp.
One McDonald Plaza
Oak Brook, IL 60521
Fred L. Turner, chairman and CEO

McDowell, Malcolm
8899 Beverly Blvd.
Los Angeles, CA 90048
Actor

McDowell, Roddy
c/o Phil Gersh Agency, Inc.
222 N. Canon Dr.
Beverly Hills, CA 90210
Actor

McEntire, Reba
Star Route
Stringtown, OK 74569
Country western singer

McGavin, Darren
8643 Holloway Plaza
Los Angeles, CA 90069
Actor

McGee, Dean Anderson
P.O. Box 25851
Oklahoma City, OK 73125
Petroleum company exec.

McGee, Willie
St. Louis Cardinals, Busch Stadium
Box 888
Saint Louis, MO 63188
Baseball player

McGhee, Walter Brownie
c/o Agency for the Performing
Arts
120 W. 57th St.
New York, NY 10019
Blues singer and guitarist

McGovern, George Stanley
c/o Arms for Common Sense
1875 Connecticut Ave. NW.
Washington, DC 20009
Former senator, presidential candidate, chairman AFCS

McGovern, Maureen
c/o Warner Brothers Records
3300 Warner Blvd.
Burbank, CA 91510
Entertainer

McGraw-Hill, Inc.
1221 Ave. of the Americas
New York, NY 10020
*Harold W. McGraw, Jr.,
chairman of the board*

McGruder, Stephen Jones
One W. 54th St.
New York, NY 10019
Portfolio manager

McGuire, Dorothy
P.O. Box 25940
Los Angeles, CA 90025
Actress

MCI Communications Corp.
1133 19th St. NW.
Washington, DC 20036
William G. McGowan, chairman

McKay, Jim
c/o ABC Sports
1330 Ave. of the Americas
New York, NY 10019
Television sports commentator

McKean, Michael
c/o Triad Artists, Inc.
10100 Santa Monica Blvd.
16th Floor
Los Angeles, CA 90067
Actor

McKuen, Rod
P.O. Box G
Beverly Hills, CA 90213
Poet, composer, author, singer

McLaughlin, Emily
1330 Ave. of the Americas
New York, NY 10019
Actress

McLaughlin, John
c/o CBS Records
51 W. 52nd St.
New York, NY 10019
Musician

McMahon, Ed
c/o NBC-TV
3000 Alameda Ave.
Burbank, CA 91505
Television announcer

THE ADDRESS BOOK

McMahon, Jim
55 E. Jackson
Chicago, IL 60604
Quarterback, Chicago Bears

McManus, William J.
310 1st St. SE.
Washington, DC 20003
Republican National Committee exec.

McMillan, Kenneth
c/o Henderson/Hogan Agency
247 S. Beverly Dr.
Beverly Hills, CA 90212
Actor

McNamara, Julianne
8285 Sunset Blvd., Suite One
Los Angeles, CA 90046
Olympic gymnast

McNamara, Robert
2412 Tracy Pl.
Washington, DC 20008
Former secretary of defense

McNeil, Freeman
598 Madison Ave.
New York, NY 10022
Football player

McNichol, Kristy
151 El Camino Dr.
Beverly Hills, CA 90212
Actress

McVie, Christine Perfect
3300 Warner Blvd.
Burbank, CA 91505
Musician, singer

McVie, John
c/o International Creative Management
40 W. 57th St.
New York, NY 10019
Musician

McWethy, John
3601 N. Dickerson St.
Arlington, VA 22207
Chief Pentagon correspondent, ABC News

Mead, Stanton Witter
P.O. Box 7
Wisconsin Rapids, WI 54494
Paper company exec.

Meade, Julia
1010 5th Ave.
New York, NY 10028
Actress

Meadows, Audrey
9744 Wilshire at Linden
Suite 308
Beverly Hills, CA 90212
Actress

Meara, Anne
c/o Phil Gersh Agency, Inc.
222 N. Canon Dr.
Beverly Hills, CA 90210
Actress

Mears, Rick
P.O. Box 2183
Bakersfield, CA 93303
Race car driver

Meatloaf
225 E. 57th St.
New York, NY 10022
Rock guitarist, singer

Medoff, Mark
P.O. Box 3072
Las Cruces, NM 88003
Playwright

Meese, Edwin III
Office of the Attorney General
10th and Constitution Ave. NW.
Washington, DC 20530
*Former attorney general of the
United States*

Mehta, Zubin
c/o New York Philharmonic,
Avery Fisher Hall
Broadway and 65th St.
New York, NY 10023
Conductor, musician

Meier, Richard Louis
7 San Mateo Rd.
Berkeley, CA 94707
*Futurist, planner, behavioral
scientist*

Melcher, John
Hart Senate Office Bldg.
Room 730
Washington, DC 20510
U.S. senator

Mellencamp, John Cougar
c/o International Creative
Management
40 W. 57th St.
New York, NY 10019
Rock singer, songwriter, musician

Melnick, Daniel
300 Colgems Square
Burbank, CA 91505
Motion picture producer

Mengers, Sue
William Morris Agency, Inc.
151 El Camino Dr.
Beverly Hills, CA 90210
Motion picture talent agent

Mensa
2626 E. 14th St.
Brooklyn, NY 11235
A high-IQ foundation

Menudo
Padosa Hato Rey
157 Ponce de Leon
San Juan, PR 00901
Pop group

Menzies, Heather
10000 Santa Monica Blvd.
Suite 305
Los Angeles, CA 90067
Actress

Mercer, Marian
c/o Susan Smith & Associates
9869 Santa Monica Blvd.
Beverly Hills, CA 90212
Actress

Meredith, Burgess
10351 Santa Monica Blvd.
2nd Floor
Los Angeles, CA 90046
Actor

Meredith, Don
Box 597
Santa Fe, NM 87501
Former football player, sports announcer, actor

Merilan, Charles Preston
c/o University of Missouri
Columbia, MO 65201
Dairy husbandry scientist

Merrill Lynch & Co., Inc.
165 Broadway
New York, NY 10006
William A. Schreyer, chairman and CEO

Merriwether, Lee
P.O. Box 402
Encino, CA 91316
Actress

Metheny, Pat
c/o Ted Kurland Associates, Inc.
173 Brighton Ave.
Boston, MA 02134
Musician

Metromedia, Inc.
One Harmon Plaza
Secaucus, NJ 07094
John W. Kluge, chairman, president, and CEO

Metzenbaum, Howard Morton
Russell Senate Office Bldg.
Room 140
Washington, DC 20510
U.S. senator

Meyer, Nicholas
2109 Stanley Hills Dr.
Los Angeles, CA 90046
Motion picture writer, director

Meyer, Russ
P.O. Box 3748
Hollywood, CA 90078
Motion picture producer, director

Meyers, Ari
15301 Ventura Blvd., Suite 345
Sherman Oaks, CA 91403
Actress

MGM/UA Entertainment Co.
10202 W. Washington Blvd.
Culver City, CA 90230
Alan Ladd, Jr., president

Miami Sound Machine
8730 Sunset Blvd., 6th Floor
Los Angeles, CA 90069
Pop music group

Michael, George
c/o Michael Lippman
9669 Oak Pass Rd.
Beverly Hills, CA 90210
Singer, songwriter

Michaels, Alan
c/o ABC Sports
1330 Ave. of the Americas
New York, NY 10019
Sports commentator

Michaels, Lorne
c/o Broadway Video
1619 Broadway
New York, NY 10019
Television writer, producer

Michelson, Bob
16663 Victory Blvd.
Van Nuys, CA 91406
Photographer

Miles, Joanna
c/o STE Representation Ltd.
211 S. Beverly Dr.
Beverly Hills, CA 90212
Actress

Miles, Vera
c/o The Craig Agency
8485 Melrose Blvd., Suite E
Los Angeles, CA 90069
Actress

Milius, John
202 N. Canon Dr.
Beverly Hills, CA 90210
Motion picture writer, director

Millar, Sally Gray
32 Fruit St.
Boston, MA 02114
Nurse

**Miller, Ann
(Lucille Ann Collier)**
132 Lasky Dr.
Beverly Hills, CA 90212
Actress, dancer, singer

Miller, Arthur
c/o International Creative
Management
40 W. 57th St.
New York, NY 10019
Playwright, author

Miller, James Clifford III
Office of Management and Budget
Old Executive Office Bldg.
Washington, DC 20503
*Director, Office of Management
and Budget*

Miller, John
2049 Century Park E., Suite 1200
Los Angeles, CA 90067
Golfer

Miller, Mildred
c/o Robert M. Gerwald
Management
58 W. 58th St.
New York, NY 10019
Recitalist, opera singer

Miller, Steve
P.O. Box 4127
Bellevue, WA 98040
Rock guitarist, songwriter

Miller, Virginia Ann
c/o The White House, Office of
First Lady
1600 Pennsylvania Ave.
Washington, DC 20500
Staff assistant, office of First Lady

Miller Brewing Co.
3939 W. Highland Blvd.
Milwaukee, WI 53201
William K. Howell,
president and CEO

Mills, Donna
1350 Ave. of the Americas
New York, NY 10019
Actress

Mills, Stephanie
P.O. Box K, Number 350
Tarzana, CA 91356
Singer

Milne, Lorus Johnson
One Garden Lane
Durham, NH 03824
Educator, naturalist, author

Milsap, Ronnie
P.O. Box 23109
Nashville, TN 37202
Country music singer, songwriter

Mindell, Dr. Earl
2020 Cotner Ave.
Los Angeles, CA 90025
Vitamin and nutrition ex-
pert, author

Minnelli, Liza
c/o International Creative
Management
40 W. 57th St.
New York, NY 10022
Singer, actress

Minnelli, Vincente
c/o Gobler & Associates
8501 Wilshire Blvd.
Beverly Hills, CA 90211
Motion picture director

Mitchell, George John
Russell Senate Office Bldg.,
Room SR-176
Washington, DC 20510
U.S. senator

Mitchum, Robert
P.O. Box 5216
Montecito, CA 93108
Actor

Mitsubishi Motor Sales of
America, Inc.
10540 Talbert Ave.
Fountain Valley, CA 92708
T. Nishina, chairman

Mitterrand, Francois
Office of the President
Paris, France
President of France

M&M/Mars
High St.
Hackettstown, NJ 07840
Howard Walker, president

Mobil Corp.
150 E. 42nd St.
New York, NY 10017
Rawleigh Warner, Jr.,
chairman and CEO

Moffat, Donald
c/o Triad Artists
10100 Santa Monica Blvd.
Los Angeles, CA 90067
Actor

Moncrief, Sidney
c/o Milwaukee Bucks
901 N. 4th St.
Milwaukee, WI 53203
Basketball player

Mondale, Walter
c/o Winston & Strawn
2550 M St., Suite 500
NW. Washington, DC 20037
Lawyer, former vice president

Money, Eddie
c/o Bill Graham Management
P.O. Box 1994
San Francisco, CA 94101
Pop singer, songwriter

The Monkees
c/o David Fishof Productions
888 7th Ave.
New York, NY 10019
Pop music group

Monroe, Bill
c/o MCA Records
70 Universal City Plaza
Universal City, CA 91608
Bluegrass musician

Montalban, Ricardo
151 El Camino Dr.
Beverly Hills, CA 90212
Actor

Montana, Joe
c/o San Francisco 49ers
711 Nevada St.
Redwood City, CA 94061
Football player

Montgomery, Elizabeth
415 N. Crescent Dr., Suite 300
Beverly Hills, CA 90210
Actress

**Montgomery Ward & Co.,
Inc.**
Montgomery Ward Plaza
Chicago, IL 60671
Bernard F. Brennan,
chairman and CEO

Montoya, Carlos
1501 Broadway, Suite 201
New York, NY 10036
Guitarist

**Monty Python's Flying
Circus**
20 Fitzroy Square
London W1P 6BB England
British comedy troupe

THE ADDRESS BOOK

The Moody Blues
c/o Weintraub Entertainment
Group
11111 Santa Monica Blvd.
20th Floor
Los Angeles, CA 90025
Rock band

Moon, Warren
P.O. Box 1516
Houston, TX 77001
Football player

Mooney, William Piatt
8 Brookside Ct.
East Brunswick, NJ 08816
Actor

Moore, Arch A., Jr.
Office of the Governor
State Capitol
Charleston, WV 25305
Governor of West Virginia

Moore, Dudley
c/o Rogers & Cowan
10000 Santa Monica Blvd.
Los Angeles, CA 90067-7007
Actor

Moore, Joseph Curtis
4210 Mossy Oak Dr.
Lakeland, FL 33805
Mammalogist

Moore, Mary Tyler
c/o Agency for the Performing
Arts
9000 Sunset Blvd., Suite 1200
Los Angeles, CA 90069
Actress

Moore, Melba
c/o Capitol Records
1750 N. Vine St.
Hollywood, CA 90028
Singer, actress

**Moore, Robin
(Robert Lowell Moore, Jr.)**
c/o Manor Books
45 E. 30th St.
New York, NY 10016
Author

Moore, Roger
c/o London Management
235/241 Regent St.
London W1 England
Actor

Moran, Erin
1888 Century Park E., Suite 1400
Los Angeles, CA 90067
Actress

Moreno, Rita
1350 Ave. of the Americas
New York, NY 10019
Actress

Morgan, Henry
c/o The Artists Group Ltd.
1930 Century Park W., Suite 303
Los Angeles, CA 90067
Actor

Morgan, Joe Leonard
Oakland-Alameda Coliseum
Oakland, CA 94621
Baseball player

Moriarty, Michael
c/o The Lantz Office
888 7th Ave.
New York, NY 10019
Actor

Morris, Garrett
c/o J. Michael Bloom Ltd.
9200 Sunset Blvd., Suite 1210
Los Angeles, CA 90069
Actor, comedian

Morris, Gary
6027 Church Dr.
Sugar Land, TX 77478
Country western musician, singer,
songwriter

Morris, William
27 W. 44th St.
New York, NY 10036
Author, columnist, editor,
lexicographer, radio and television
broadcaster

Morrison, Margo
3650 Clark Ave., Penthouse E
Burbank, CA 91505
President, Murder Mystery
Weekends, a company that sells
and plans mystery parties
for groups

Morrison, Morris
704 Trinity
Lockheart, TX 78644
Poetry therapist

Morrison, Van
c/o Stan Diamond
12304 Santa Monica, Suite 300
W. Los Angeles, CA 90025
Singer, composer, musician

Moseley, Mark
P.O. Box 17247
Washington, DC 20041
Football player

Moses, Edwin
1750 E. Boulder St.
Colorado Springs, CO 80909
Olympic athlete

Moss, Arnold
301 E. 66th St.
New York, NY 10021
Actor, producer, writer, director

Motel 6, Inc.
51 Hitchcock Way
Santa Barbara, CA 93105
Roger C. Royce,
president and CEO

Motley Crue
c/o McGhee Entertainment
240 Central Park S., Suite 2C
New York, NY 10019
Heavy metal rock band

Moynihan, Daniel Patrick
United States Senate
Washington, DC 20510
U.S. senator, educator

Mrs. Fields Cookies
333 Main St.
Park City, UT 84640
Deborah Fields, president

Mrs. Smith's Frozen Foods Co.
South and Charlotte Sts.
Pottstown, PA 19464
A. G. Langbow,
president and CEO

MTV Networks, Inc.
1775 Broadway
New York, NY 10019
D. H. Horowitz,
president and CEO

Mubarak, Hosni
Office of the President
Cairo, Egypt
President of Egypt

Mudd, Roger
4001 Nebraska Ave.
Washington, DC 20016
Broadcast journalist

Muldaur, Diana
c/o Alexander Tucker
9200 Sunset Blvd.
Los Angeles, CA 90069
Actress

Mulgrew, Kate
9220 Sunset Blvd., Garden Suite B
Los Angeles, CA 90069
Actress

Mull, Martin
9000 Sunset Blvd., Suite 1200
Los Angeles, CA 90069
Actor

Mulligan, Richard
c/o Litske-Grossbart Management
Ltd.
8500 Wilshire Blvd.
Beverly Hills, CA 90210
Actor

Mulroney, Brian
24 Sussex Dr.
Ottawa, ON. K1M OM5
Canada
Prime minister of Canada

Monoz, Michael
200 Riverfront Stadium
Cincinnati, OH 45202
Football player

Murdoch, Rupert
c/o News Corp. Ltd.
210 South St.
New York, NY 10002
Publisher

Murkowski, Frank Hughes
Hart Senate Office Bldg.
Room 709
Washington, DC 20510
U.S. senator

Murphy, Dale
P.O. Box 4064
Atlanta, GA 30302
Baseball player

Murphy, Eddie
c/o Eddie Murphy Productions,
Inc.
232 E. 63rd St.
New York, NY 10021
Actor, comedian

Murphy, Michael
1888 Century Park E., Suite 1400
Los Angeles, CA 90067
Actor

Murphy, Rosemary
220 E. 73rd St.
New York, NY 10021
Actress

Murray, Anne
c/o Balmur Ltd.
4881 Yonge St., Suite 412
Toronto, ON. M2N 5X3
Canada
Singer

Murray, Bill
1888 Century Park E., Suite 1400
Los Angeles, CA 90067
Actor, writer, comedian

Murray, Donald Patrick
1900 Wilshire Blvd., Suite 900
Los Angeles, CA 90057
Actor

Murray, Jim
8899 Beverly Blvd.
Los Angeles, CA 90048
Personal appearance agent

Murray, Joan Elizabeth
4525 Valley Ridge
Los Angeles, CA 90008
*Broadcaster, author, business-
woman*

Musburger, Brent
c/o CBS Sports
51 W. 52nd St.
New York, NY 10019
Sportscaster

**Muscular Dystrophy
Association**
810 7th Ave.
New York, NY 10019
Jerry Lewis, national chairman

Musicland Group
7500 Excelsior Blvd.
Minneapolis, MN 55426
Jack W. Eugster, president

Myers, George Elliot
1339 Pomona Rd.
Ann Arbor, MI 48103
Prosthodontist

Myers, Russel
c/o Tribune Media Services, Inc.
770 N. Orange Ave.
Orlando, FL 32801
*Cartoonist, creator of
"Broom Hilda"*

Myhers, John
9200 Sunset Blvd., Suite 808
Los Angeles, CA 90069
Actor, writer, director

Nabisco Brands, Inc.
Nabisco Brands Plaza
Parsippany, NJ 07054
James O. Welch, president

Nabors, Jim
c/o CBS Records, Inc.
51 W. 52nd St.
New York, NY 10019
Actor, singer

Nachman, Gerald Weil
901 Mission St.
San Francisco, CA 94103
Columnist, author

Nader, Ralph
P.O. Box 19367
Washington, DC 20036
*Consumer advocate,
lawyer, author*

Nalley's Fine Foods
3303 35th St.
Tacoma, WA 98411
*J. William Petty,
president and CEO*

Namath, Joe
c/o The Lantz Office
888 7th Ave.
New York, NY 10106
Entertainer, former football player

Nash, Graham
c/o Hartman & Goodman
1500 Crossroads of the World
Hollywood, CA 90028
Singer, songwriter

National Broadcasting Company (NBC)
30 Rockefeller Plaza
New York, NY 10020
Grant Tinker, chairman and CEO

National Car Rental System
7700 France Ave.
S. Minneapolis, MN 55435
Bemiss A. Rolfs, president

National Hobo Association
World Way Center
Box 90430
Los Angeles, CA 90009
Bob Hopkins, founding director

National Organization Taunting Safety and Fairness Everywhere (N.O.T.S.A.F.E.)
P.O. Box 5743
Montecito, CA 93108
Dale Lowdermilk, founder. Organization designed for safely venting frustrations at stupid laws

National Socialist White People's Party
2507 N. Franklin Rd.
Arlington, VA 22201
Commander Matt Koehl

National Steel Corp.
20 Stanwix St.
Pittsburgh, PA 15222
Howard M. Love,
chairman and CEO

Natzler, Otto
7873 Woodrow Wilson Dr.
Los Angeles, CA 90046
Ceramic artist

Navratilova, Martina
c/o U.S. Tennis Association
51 E. 42nd St.
New York, NY 10017
Tennis player

NCR Corp.
1700 S. Patterson Blvd.
Dayton, OH 45479
Charles E. Exley, Jr.,
chairman and CEO

Neal, Patricia
P.O. Box 1043
Edgartown, MA 02539
Actress

Nebenzahl, Kenneth
135 Crescent Dr.
Glencoe, IL 60022
Rare book and map dealer

Needham, Hal
3518 Cahuenga Blvd. W.
Suite 110
Los Angeles, CA 90068
Motion picture writer, director

Neff, Francine Irving
1509 Sagebrush Trail SE.
Albuquerque, NM 87123
Former treasurer of the U.S.

Negroponte, John Dimitri
Embassy of the United States
Avenida La Paz
Tegucigalpa, Honduras
U.S. ambassador

Neiman, Leroy
One W. 67th St.
New York, NY 10023
Artist

Neiman Marcus
Main and Ervay Sts.
Dallas, TX 75201
Richard C. Marcus, chairman

**Nelligan, Kate
(Patricia Colleen Nelligan)**
c/o Larry Dalzell Associates
3 Goodwin's Ct.
London WC2 England
Actress

Nelson, Barry
c/o William Morris Agency
1350 Ave. of the Americas
New York, NY 10019
Actor

Nelson, Harriet
c/o Cary Management
13263 Ventura Blvd.
Studio City, CA 91604
Actress

Nelson, Lindsay
c/o International Creative
Management
40 W. 57th St.
New York, NY 10019
Sportscaster

**Nemetz, Nathaniel
Theodore**
Law Courts
800 Smithe St.
Vancouver, BC. V6Z 2E1
Canada
Chief justice of British Columbia

Ness, Norman Frederick
c/o NASA Goddard Space Flight
Center
Greenbelt, MD 20770
Space scientist

Nestle Foods Corp.
100 Manhattanville Rd.
Purchase, NY 10577
*C. A. MacDonald, president and
CEO*

Nettleton, Lois
c/o William Morris Agency
1350 Ave. of the Americas
New York, NY 10019
Actress

Neutrogena Corp.
5755 W. 96th St.
Los Angeles, CA 90045
*Lloyd E. Costen, president and
CEO*

Nevil, Robbie
c/o NuVision Entertainment
9200 Sunset Blvd., Penthouse 15
Los Angeles, CA 90069
Singer, songwriter

New Edition
c/o Guardian Productions, Inc.
161 W. 54th St.
New York, NY 10019
Pop music group

Newell, Gregory John
7381 Hallcrest Dr.
McLean, VA 22101
U.S. ambassador to Sweden

Newhart, Bob
315 S. Beverly Dr.
Beverly Hills, CA 90212
Actor

Newley, Anthony
4419 Van Nuys Blvd.
Sherman Oaks, CA 91403
Actor, singer

Newlin, Michael H.
U.S. Embassy
4 Chemin Cheich
Bachir, Brahimi
Algiers, Algeria
U.S. ambassador

Newman, Barry
c/o Mason & Co.
400 Park Ave.
New York, NY 10022
Actor

Newman, David
250 W. 57th St., Room 1430
New York, NY 10017
Writer

Newman, Edwin
c/o NBC-TV
30 Rockefeller Plaza
New York, NY 10112
Retired news commentator

Newman, Randy
c/o Renaissance Management
Corp.
433 N. Camden Dr.
Beverly Hills, CA 90210
Singer, songwriter, musician

Newman, William Stein
800 Old Mill Road
Chapel Hill, NC 27514
Composer, pianist

Newsmaker Interviews
439 S. La Cienega, Number 219
Los Angeles, CA 90048
Arthur Levine, publisher. Newsletter advises radio stations who's available for interviews

Newsweek, Inc.
444 Madison Ave.
New York, NY 10022
Mark M. Edmiston, president

Newton, David George
c/o American Embassy
P.O. Box 2447
Alwiyah Baghdad, Iraq
U.S. ambassador to Iraq

Newton, Juice
P.O. Box 7308
Carmel, CA 93921
Country singer

Newton, Natalie
c/o Winners International
Investments
157 Whooping Loop
Altamonte Springs, FL 32701
Syndicated columnist

Newton, Wayne
3180 S. Highland Dr.
Number One
Las Vegas, NV 89109-1042
Entertainer

Newton-John, Olivia
P.O. Box 2020
Newbury Park, CA 91320
Singer, actress

New York Stock Exchange, Inc.
11 Wall St.
New York, NY 10005
John J. Phelan, Jr., chairman

The New York Times Co.
229 W. 43rd St.
New York, NY 10036
Walter Mattson, president

Ngonda, Putteho Muketoi
c/o Zambian Embassy
2419 Massachusetts Ave.
NW. Washington, DC 20008
Zambian ambassador to the U.S.

Nicholson, Jack
c/o The Artists Agency
190 N. Canon Dr.
Beverly Hills, CA 90210
Actor

Nicklaus, Jack
1208 U.S. Highway One
North Palm Beach, FL 33408
Golfer

Nickles, Don
Hart Senate Office Bldg.
Room 713
Washington, DC 20510
U.S. senator

Nicks, Stevie
8899 Beverly Blvd.
Los Angeles, CA 90048
Singer, songwriter

Niekro, Joe
Minnesota Twins
501 Chicago Ave. South
Minneapolis, MN 55415
Baseball player

Nielsen, Erik H.
Office of Deputy Prime Minister
Parliament Bldg.

Ottawa, ON. K1A 0A2
Canada
Deputy prime minister of Canada

Nigh, George
Office of Governor
212 State Capitol
Oklahoma City, OK 73105
Governor of Oklahoma

Night Ranger
c/o Bruce Cohn Management
P.O. Box 878
Sonoma, CA 95476
Rock bank

Nike, Inc.
3900 SW. Murray Blvd.
Beaverton, OR 97005
Philip H. Knight,
chairman, president, and CEO

Nikolais, Alwin
c/o Nikolais/Louis Foundation for
Dance, Inc.
33 E. 18th St.
New York, NY 10003
Choreographer

Niles, Thomas Michael Tolliver
c/o U.S. Embassy
200 Wellington St.
Ottawa, ON. K1P5T1
Canada
U.S. ambassador to Canada

Nilsson, Harry
c/o RCA Records
1133 Ave. of the Americas
New York, NY 10036
Singer, songwriter

Nitty Gritty Dirt Band
P.O. Box 6106
Branson, MO 65616
Country music group

Nixon, Richard Milhous
26 Federal Plaza
New York, NY 10278
Former president of the U.S.

Noble, James
c/o Triad Artists
10100 Santa Monica Blvd.
Los Angeles, CA 90067
Actor

Nolte, Nick
8899 Beverly Blvd.
Los Angeles, CA 90048
Actor

Nordstrom, Inc.
1501 5th Ave.
Seattle, WA 98101
James F. Nordstrom, president

Norris, Chuck
17300 17th St., Suite 251
Tustin, CA 92680
Actor, martial arts expert

North, Alex
630 Resolano Dr.
Pacific Palisades, CA 90272
Composer

North American Van Lines, Inc.
5001 U.S. Highway 30 W.
Fort Wayne, IN 46801
Kenneth W. Maxfield, chairman and president

Northrop Corp.
1840 Century Park E.
Los Angeles, CA 90067
Thomas V. Jones, chairman and CEO

Northwest Airlines, Inc.
Minneapolis-St. Paul International Airport
St. Paul, MN 55111
Steven J. Rothmeier, president and CEO

Norton-Taylor, Judy
135 Screenland Dr.
Toluca Lake, CA 91505
Actress

Novak, James A.
P.O. Box 241532
Los Angeles, CA 90024
President, Letterdial, a company that uses phone prefixes and area codes to make personalized phone numbers

Novak, Kim (Marilyn Novak)
c/o Agency for Performing Arts
120 W. 57th St.
New York, NY 10019
Actress

**Novello, Don
(Father Guido Sarduchi)**
8899 Beverly Blvd.
Los Angeles, CA 90048
Writer, comedian, producer

**Nugent, Ted
(Theodore Anthony Nugent)**
c/o CBS/Epic Records
51 W. 52nd St.
New York, NY 10019
Rock guitarist, songwriter

Nunn, Sam
Dirksen Senate Office Bldg.,
Room 303
Washington, DC 20510
U.S. senator

Nureyev, Rudolf
c/o Paris Opera Ballet
8 Rue Scribe
Paris F-75009 France
Ballet dancer, ballet company exec.

Nu Shooz
c/o Sosumi, Inc.
3233 SW. Newby Terrace
Portland, OR 97201
Pop music group

The NutraSweet Co.
P.O. Box 1111
Skokie, IL 60076
Robert B. Shapiro, president and CEO

**Nutzle, Futzie
(Bruce John Kleinsmith)**
P.O. Box 325
Aromas, CA 95004
Cartoonist

Oakley, Robert
c/o State Department
2201 C St.
NW. Washington, DC 20520
*Acting ambassador-at-large for
counter/terrorism*

The Oak Ridge Boys
329 Rockland Rd.
Hendersonville, TN 37075
Country western group

Oates, John
130 W. 57th St., Suite 12B
New York, NY 10019
Singer, songwriter

O'Brian, Hugh
132 Lasky Dr.
Beverly Hills, CA 90212
*Actor, founder of the Hugh
O'Brian Youth Foundation*

O'Brien, Ken
1265 Lombardi Ave.
Green Bay, WI 54304
Football player

O'Brien, Lawrence Francis
860 United Nations Plaza
New York, NY 10017
*Former basketball commissioner,
former chairman, Democratic National Committee*

**O'Brien, Margaret
(Angela Maxine O'Brien)**
c/o Mark Levin Associates
328 S. Beverly Dr., Suite E
Beverly Hills, CA 90212
Actress

O'Brien, Thomas Joseph
400 E. Monroe
Phoenix, AZ 85004
*Catholic Bishop of Phoenix,
Arizona*

**Occidental Petroleum
Corp.**
10889 Wilshire Blvd.
Los Angeles, CA 90024
*Armand Hammer,
chairman and CEO*

Ocean, Billy
c/o International Creative
Management
40 W. 57th St.
New York, NY 10019
Singer

**Ocean Spray Cranberries,
Inc.**
225 Water St.
Plymouth, MA 02360
Harold Thorkilsen, president

O'Connor, Carroll
P.O. Box 49935
Los Angeles, CA 90049-0935
Actor, writer, producer

O'Connor, Sandra Day
c/o Supreme Court of the
United States
One 1st St.
NE. Washington, DC 20543
Justice, U.S. Supreme Court

O'Day, Anita Belle Colton
P.O. Box 123
North Haven, CT 06473
Entertainer, singer

Oehser, Paul Henry
9012 Old Dominion Dr.
McLean, VA 22102
Conservationist, editor, writer

Oingo Boingo
8335 Sunset Blvd., 3rd Floor
W. Hollywood, CA 90069
Pop music band

O'Keefe, Miles
P.O. Box 69365
Los Angeles, CA 90069
Actor

King Olaf V
Royal Palace
Oslo, Norway
King of Norway

Oldsmobile
920 Townshend St.
Lansing, MI 48933
William W. Lane, general manager

Olivier, Laurence
c/o LOP Ltd.
33-34 Chancery Ln.
London WC2 A 1EW England
Actor, director

Olmos, Edward James
10000 Santa Monica Blvd.
Suite 305
Los Angeles, CA 90067
Actor

Olsen, Merlin
c/o NBC Sports
30 Rockefeller Plaza
New York, NY 10112
*Sports analyst, former football
player*

**OMD (Orchestral Maneu-
vers in the Dark)**
c/o ICM
40 W. 57th St.
New York, NY 10019
Pop music group

**Onassis, Jacqueline Bou-
vier Kennedy**
c/o Doubleday & Co.
245 Park Ave.
New York, NY 10017
*Editor, widow of 35th president
of the United States*

O'Neal, Frederick
165 W. 46th St.
New York, NY 10036
Actor, lecturer, director

O'Neal, Ryan
1888 Century Park E., Suite 1400
Los Angeles, CA 90067
Actor

O'Neil, Kitty
P.O. Box 604
Medina, OH 44256
Stuntwoman, motor sport racer

O'Neill, William
Office of Governor, State Capitol,
Room 202
Hartford, CT 06115
Governor of Connecticut

Orbach, Jerry
132 Lasky Dr.
Beverly Hills, CA 90212
Actor, singer

Orben, Robert
1200 North Nash St.
Number 1122
Arlington, VA 22209
Author, editor of Orben's Current Comedy, a humor service providing topical jokes to emcees, speakers, etc.

Order, Stanley Elias
c/o Johns Hopkins Hospital
600 N. Wolfe St.

Baltimore, MD 21205
Radiation scientist educator

Ore-Ida Foods Co., Inc.
P.O. Box 10
Boise, ID 83707
Paul Cordory, president

Orlandini, S.
c/o KLM Royal Dutch Airlines
437 Madison Ave.
New York, NY 10022
President, KLM Royal Dutch Airlines

Orr, Bobby (Robert Gordon Orr)
647 Summer St.
Boston, MA 02210
Retired hockey player

Orr, Robert Dunkerson
Office of Governor
State Capitol
Indianapolis, IN 46204
Governor of Indiana

Ortega, Katherine D.
c/o Department of Treasury
Main Treasury Bldg., Room 4328
Washington, DC 20220
Treasurer of the U.S.

Osborne, Jeffrey
10100 Santa Monica Blvd.
16th Floor
Los Angeles, CA 90067
Singer, songwriter

Osborne, John James
c/o Fraser & Dunlop
91 Regent St.
London W1 England
Playwright

Osborne, Tom
c/o Nebraska Sports Information
116 South Stadium
Lincoln, NE 68588
*Coach, Nebraska Cornhuskers
football team*

Osbourne, Ozzy
c/o International Creative
Management
40 W. 57th St.
New York, NY 10019
Heavy metal rock singer

Oscar Mayer & Co.
P.O. Box 7188
Madison, WI 53707
*Jerry M. Hiegel,
chairman and CEO*

Osgood, Charles
c/o CBS News
524 W. 57th St.
New York, NY 10019
Broadcast journalist

The Osmond Family
3325 N. University Ave.
Provo, UT 84604-4438
Entertainers

**Osterwald, Bibi
(Margaret Virginia)**
c/o Contemporary Artists Ltd.
132 Lasky Dr.
Beverly Hills, CA 90212
Actress

O'Toole, Peter
1350 Ave. of the Americas
New York, NY 10019
Actor

The Outfield
P.O. Box 1994
San Francisco, CA 94101
Pop music band

Overeaters Anonymous
4025 Spencer St., Number 203
Torrence, CA 90503
Attn: General information

**Owens, Buck
(Alvis Edgar, Jr.)**
1225 N. Chester Ave.
Bakersfield, CA 93308
Singer, musician, songwriter

Owens, Gary
18107 Lake Encino Dr.
Encino, CA 91316
*Radio and television performer,
author*

Owens, Roger
5216 Onyx St.
Torrance, CA 90503
The Peanut Man

Owens-Corning Fiberglass Corp.
Fiberglass Tower
Toldeo, OH 43604
*William Boeschenstein,
chairman of the board*

Oz, Frank
c/o Henson Associates
117 E. 69th St.
New York, NY 10024
Puppeteer, actor

Pabst Brewing Co.
P.O. Box 766
Milwaukee, WI 53201
Lutz E. Isseib, chairman

Pacific Southwest Airlines (PSA), Inc.
3225 N. Harbor Dr.
San Diego, CA 92101
*Paul C. Barkley,
president and CEO*

Pacino, Al
c/o The Actors Studio
432 W. 44th St.
New York, NY 10036
Actor

Packwood, Bob
Russell Senate Office Bldg.,
Room 259
Washington, DC 20510
U.S. senator

Page, James Patrick
c/o Swan Song Inc.
444 Madison Ave.
New York, NY 10022
Guitarist, composer

Page, Patti
P.O. Box 1105
Rancho Santa Fe, CA 92067
Singer

Page, Ruth
c/o Ruth Page Foundation School
for Dance
1016 N. Dearborn St.
Chicago, IL 60610
Dancer, director

Paige, Satchel
2626 E. 28th St.
Kansas City, MO 64128
Former baseball player

Paine Webber, Inc.
1285 Ave. of the Americas
New York, NY 10019
*Donald B. Marron,
chairman and CEO*

Paley, William S.
c/o CBS
51 W. 52nd St.
New York, NY 10019
Broadcasting executive, consultant

Palmer, Arnold
Box 52
Youngstown, PA 15696
Golfer

Palmer, James Alvin
c/o ABC-TV Sports
1330 Ave. of the Americas
New York, NY 10019
Sportscaster

Palmer, Lilli
c/o Harper & Row, Inc.
10 E. 53rd St.
New York, NY 10022
Actress, author

Palmer, Robert
10100 Santa Monica Blvd.
16th Floor
Los Angeles, CA 90067
Rock singer, songwriter

Pan Am Corp.
200 Park Ave.
New York, NY 10166
L. E. Acker, chairman and CEO

Panasonic Co.
One Panasonic Way
Secaucus, NJ 07094
Akiyu Imura, president and CEO

Papas, Irene
c/o United Film Distribution Co.
115 Middle Neck Rd.
Great Neck, NY 11021
Actress

Papp, Joseph
c/o New York Shakespeare
Festival
425 Lafayette St.
New York, NY 10003
Theater producer, director

Paramount Pictures Corp.
One Gulf and Western Plaza
New York, NY 10023
*Frank Mancuso,
chairman and CEO*

**Parapsychology Institute
of America**
P.O. Box 252
Elmhurst, NY 11380
Dr. Stephen Kaplan

**Pardo, Don
(Dominick George Pardo)**
c/o NBC
30 Rockefeller Plaza, Room 607W
New York, NY 10112
Broadcasting announcer

Parish, Robert
c/o Boston Celtics
Boston Garden, North Station
Boston, MA 02114
Basketball player

Parker, Alan
c/o Alan Parker Film Co.
Pinewood Studios
Iver Heath
Buckinghamshire, England
Motion picture director

Parker, Brant
c/o News American Syndicate
1703 Kaiser Ave.
Irvine, CA 92714
Cartoonist

Parker, David
Oakland A's
P.O. Box 2220
Oakland, CA 94621
Baseball player

Parker, Jameson
10100 Santa Monica Blvd.
16th Floor
Los Angeles, CA 90067
Actor

Parker, George M.
1440 S. Byrne Rd.
Toledo, OH 43416
*President, American Flint Glass
Workers Union*

Parker, Ray, Jr.
11340 W. Olympic Blvd.
Suite 357
Los Angeles, CA 90064
*Singer, songwriter, musician,
producer*

Parks, Bert
c/o Dean Parker Abrams-Rubaloff
9012 Beverly Blvd.
Los Angeles, CA 90048
Entertainer

Parseghian, Ara Raoul
c/o CBS Sports
51 W. 52nd St.
New York, NY 10019
*Former football coach, sports
commentator*

Parsons, Estelle
505 West End Ave.
New York, NY 10024
Actress

Parton, Dolly Rebecca
8730 Sunset Blvd., Penthouse W.
Los Angeles, CA 90069
Entertainer

Pate, Jerome Kendrick
P.O. Box 1790
Pensacola, FL 32598-1790
Golfer

Patrick, Dennis
328 S. Beverly Dr., Suite E
Beverly Hills, CA 90212
Actor

**Patrick, Ruth
(Mrs. Charles Hodge)**
c/o Academy of Natural Sciences
Philadelphia, PA 19103
*Limnologist, diatom taxonomist,
educator*

Patterson, Dick
c/o Artist Career Management
8295 Sunset Blvd.
Los Angeles, CA 90046
Artist, actor

Patterson, Floyd
P.O. Box 336
New Paltz, NY 12561
*Former heavyweight boxing
champ, athletic commissioner*

Pauley, Jane
c/o NBC
30 Rockefeller Plaza
New York, NY 10112
Host, The Today Show

Pavarotti, Luciano
c/o Herbert Breslin
119 W. 57th St.
New York, NY 10019
Lyric tenor

Paxton, Tom
5109 Oak Haven Ln.
Tampa, FL 33617
Songwriter, entertainer

Paycheck, Johnny
38 Music Square E., Suite 300
Nashville, TN 37203
Country music singer, songwriter

Payton, Walter
55 E. Jackson St., Suite 1200
Chicago, IL 60604
Football player

Payton-Wright, Pamela
8899 Beverly Blvd.
Los Angeles, CA 90048
Actress

Peace Corps
806 Connecticut Ave.
Washington, DC 20006
Redmond Hogan

Peale, Norman Vincent
1025 5th Ave.
New York, NY 10028
Clergyman, author

**Pearl, Minnie
(Sarah Colley Cannon)**
c/o Jim Halsey Co., Inc.
3225 S. Norwood St.
Tulsa, OK 74135
Entertainer

Peck, Gregory
375 No. Carolwood
Los Angeles, CA 90024
Actor

Peiperi, Adam
1135 Loxford Terrace
Silver Spring, MD 20901
Kinetic sculptor and video artist

**Pele
(Arantes Do Nascimento
Edson)**
75 Rockefeller Plaza
New York, NY 10019
Soccer player

Pell, Claiborne
Russell Senate Office Bldg.
Room 335
Washington, DC 20510
U.S. senator

Pelletier, Jean
Hotel De Dille
Rue Desjardins
Quebec PQ G1R 4S9
Canada
Mayor of Quebec

Pena, Frederico Fabian
350 City and County Bldg.
Denver, CO 80202
Mayor of Denver

Pena, Tony
St. Louis Cardinals Busch Memorial Stadium
250 Stadium Plaza
St. Louis, MO 63102
Baseball player

Pendergrass, Teddy
P.O. Box 243
Gladwyne, PA 19035
Musician, singer, songwriter

Pendleton, Austin
c/o The Artists Agency
190 N. Canon Dr.
Beverly Hills, CA 90210
Actor, director

Penn, Sean
1888 Century Park E., Suite 1400
Los Angeles, CA 90067
Actor

Pennzoil Co.
P.O. Box 2967
Houston, TX 77252
*J. Hugh Liedtke,
chairman and CEO*

Penthouse International, Ltd.
1965 Broadway
New York, NY 10023
*Bob Guccione,
chairman, president, and CEO*

People for the Ethical Treatment of Animals
P.O. Box 42516
Washington, DC 20015
Attn: General information

People for Responsible Management of Radiation Waste
c/o Roxbury Medical Group
Saccassuma, NJ 07876
Walter Burnstein, Collen McGrath, founders

The Pep Boys
32nd and Allegheny
Philadelphia, PA 19132
*Benjamin Strauss,
chairman, president, and CEO*

Peppard, George
P.O. Box 1643
Beverly Hills, CA 90213
Actor

Pepperidge Farm, Inc.
P.O. Box 5500
Norwalk, CT 06856
W. A. Schmidt, president

Pepsico, Inc.
Anderson Hill Rd.
Purchase, NY 10577
*Donald M. Kendall,
chairman and CEO*

Peres, Shimon
Office of the Prime Minister
Jerusalem, Israel
Prime minister of Israel

Perkins, Anthony
8899 Beverly Blvd.
Los Angeles, CA 90048
Actor

Perkins, Ray
Box K, 2nd Floor
Memorial Coliseum
University, AL 35486
College football coach

Perlman, Rhea
c/o NBC Press Dept.
30 Rockefeller Plaza
New York, NY 10112
Actress

Perpich, Rudy George
Office of the Governor
Capitol Bldg., Room 130
Saint Paul, MN 55155
Governor of Minnesota

Perrine, Valerie
9000 Sunset Blvd., Suite 315
Los Angeles, CA 90069
Actress

Perry, Gaylord
515 Oakwood Ave.
Raleigh, NC 27604
Former baseball player

Perry, Paul
121 Meramec St.

Clayton, MO 63105
Flavor chemist

Peter Paul Cadbury
New Haven Rd.
Naugatuck, CT 06770
J. A. Hanlon, president

**Peters, Bernadette
(Bernadette Lazzara)**
8500 Wilshire Blvd., Suite 520
Beverly Hills, CA 90211
Actress

Peters, Brock
12750 Ventura Blvd., Suite 102
Studio City, CA 91604
Actor, singer, producer

Peterson, Lloyd
2425 S. Progress Dr.
Salt Lake City, UT 84119
*President, Metro Business Con-
sultants, Inc. Marketers of the first
microwave popcorn vending
machines*

Peterson, Mildred Othmer
5834 Stoney Island Ave.
Chicago, IL 60637
*Lecturer, writer, librarian, civic
leader*

Peterson, Roger Tory
c/o Houghton-Mifflin Co.
2 Park St.
Boston, MA 02108
Ornithologist, artist

The Pet Shop Boys
10100 Santa Monica Blvd.
16th Floor
Los Angeles, CA 90067
Pop music group

Petty, Richard
Route 3, Box 621
Randleman, NC 27317
Auto racer

Petty, Tom
c/o Lookout Management
8919 Sunset Blvd.
Los Angeles, CA 90069
Rock guitarist, singer, songwriter

Petzoldt, Paul Kiesow
Route One, Box 74M
Tetonia, ID 83452
Mountaineer

Peyser, Penny
8899 Beverly Blvd.
Los Angeles, CA 90048
Actress

Pfeiffer, Michelle
13794 Beach Blvd.
Westminster, CA 92683
Actress

Prince Philip
Buckingham Palace
London SW1 England
Duke of Edinburgh

Phillips, Julia
Box 900
Beverly Hills, CA 90213
Motion picture producer

**Phillips, Dail Andres
(Bum Phillips)**
1500 Poydras St.
New Orleans, LA 70112
Football coach

Phillips, Susan
2033 K St., Room 800
NW. Washington, DC 20581
*Chairman, Commodity Futures
Trading Commission*

Phoenix, River
c/o BOP
P.O. Box 2592
Hollywood, CA 90078
Actor, guitarist

Piedmont Aviation, Inc.
Smith-Reynolds Airport
Winston-Salem, NC 27156
*William R. Howard,
president and CEO*

Piercy, Marge
P.O. Box 943
Wellfleet, MA 02667
Poet, essayist, novelist

Pierpoint, Robert Charles
2020 M St.
Washington, DC 20036
*CBS News national security
correspondent*

Piggy, Miss
117 E. 69th St.
New York, NY 10021
Muppet, in love with Kermit

Pillsbury Co.
200 S. 6th St.
Minneapolis, MN 55402
John M. Stafford,
president, chairman, and CEO

Piniella, Louis Victor
c/o New York Yankees,
Yankee Stadium
Bronx, NY 10451
Former baseball player

Pinter, Harold
c/o ACTAC
16 Cadogon Ln.
London, SW1 England
Playwright

Pioneer Pete
200 S. 6th St.
Minneapolis, MN 55402
Pioneer Chicken spokesman

Piscopo, Joseph Charles
1888 Century Park E., Suite 1400
Los Angeles, CA 90067
Actor, writer, comedian

Pizza Hut, Inc.
9111 E. Douglas
Wichita, KS 67207
Arthur G. Gunther,
president and CEO

Place, Mary Kay
9744 Wilshire Blvd., Suite 206
Beverly Hills, CA 90212
Actress

Plant, Robert Anthony
c/o Atlantic Records, Swan
Song, Inc.
75 Rockefeller Plaza
New York, NY 10019
Rock singer, formerly with
Led Zeppelin

Playboy Enterprises, Inc.
919 N. Michigan Ave.
Chicago, IL 60611
Hugh M. Hefner,
chairman and CEO

Player, Gary
c/o International Management
Group
One Erieview Plaza
Cleveland, OH 44114
Golfer

Pleasance, Donald
211 S. Beverly Dr., Suite 201
Beverly Hills, CA 90212
Actor

Plimpton, George
541 E. 72nd St.
New York, NY 10021
Author, editor, television host

Plummer, Amanda
15760 Ventura Blvd.
Number 1730
Encino, CA 91436
Actress

Plummer, Christopher
8899 Beverly Blvd.
Los Angeles, CA 90048
Actor

Plunkett, James William, Jr.
c/o Los Angeles Raiders
322 Center St.
El Segundo, CA 90245
Football player

Pohl, Frederick
855 S. Harvard Dr.
Palatine, IL 60067
Writer

The Pointer Sisters
8730 Sunset Blvd., Penthouse W.
Los Angeles, CA 90069
Pop music group

Poison
6777 Hollywood Blvd., 6th Floor
Hollywood, CA 90028
Glam-rock band

Poitier, Sidney
c/o Verdon Productions
9350 Wilshire Blvd.
Beverly Hills, CA 90212
Actor, singer

Polanski, Roman
c/o Bureau Georges Beaume
3 quai Malaquais
Paris 75006 France
Motion picture writer, actor, and director

Polaroid Corp.
549 Technology Sq.
Cambridge, MA 02139
William J. McCune, Jr., chairman and CEO

Pollack, Sydney
1888 Century Park E., Suite 1400
Los Angeles, CA 90067
Motion picture director

Polo Fashions, Inc.
770 Central Blvd.
Carlstadt, NJ 07072
Ralph Lauren, chairman

**Pop, Iggy
(James Jewell Osterberg)**
449 S. Beverly Dr., Number 102
Beverly Hills, CA 90212
Rock singer, songwriter

Popsicle Industries, Inc.
110 Route 4
Englewood, NJ 07631
Rupert A. Walters, president and CEO

Porter, Darrell
P.O. Box 1111
Arlington, TX 76010
Baseball player

Poston, Tom
Contemporary Artists Ltd.
132 Lasky Dr.
Beverly Hills, CA 90212
Actor

Povich, Shirley Lewis
c/o *Washington Post*
1515 L St. NW.
Washington, DC 20005
Columnist

Powell, Lewis Franklin, Jr.
U.S. Supreme Court
One 1st St.
NE. Washington, DC 20543
Associate justice, U.S. Supreme Court

Powell, Randolph Marlin
c/o The Gersh Agency
222 N. Canon Dr.
Beverly Hills, CA 90210
Actor

Power, Jed
P.O. Box 3502
Peabody, MA 01960
President, Cape Ann Antiques, first business specializing in drug antiques and collectibles

Power, Jules
78 Red Hill Circle
Tiburon, CA 94920
Television producer

Powers, Mala
135 W. 50th St., 12th Floor
New York, NY 10020
Actress

Powers, Stephanie
8899 Beverly Blvd.
Los Angeles, CA 90048
Actress

Prager, Dennis
2265 Westwood Blvd., Suite 312
Los Angeles, CA 90064
Publisher of Ultimate Issues, *a quarterly newsletter that addresses the great issues of our time*

Pressler, Larry
Russell Senate Office Bldg.,
Room 407A
Washington, DC 20510
U.S. senator

The Pretenders
c/o Premier Talent Agency
3 E. 54th St.
New York, NY 10022
Rock band

Previn, Andre
c/o Los Angeles Philharmonic
135 N. Grand Ave.
Los Angeles, CA 90012
Composer, conductor

Price, Ray
P.O. Box 30384
Dallas, TX 75230
Singer

Price, Vincent
9169 Sunset Blvd.
Los Angeles, CA 90069
Actor

Pride, Charley
5924 Royal Ln., Suite 104
Dallas, TX 75230
Singer

Prince (Prince Rogers Nelson)
11355 W. Olympic Blvd.
Suite 555
Los Angeles, CA 90064
Musician, songwriter, actor

Principal, Victoria
c/o Lorimar Productions
10202 Washington Blvd.
Culver City, CA 90232
Actress

Prine, John
4121 Wilshire Blvd., Suite 215
Los Angeles, CA 90010
Singer, songwriter

Procrastinators' Club of America
1405 Locust St., 11th Floor
Philadelphia, PA 19102
Les Waas, president

Procter & Gamble Co.
300 E. 6th St.
Cincinnati, OH 45202

John G. Smale,
president and CEO

Progresso Foods Corp.
365 W. Passaic St.
Rochelle Park, NJ 07662
Gaspar Taormina, CEO

Proxmire, William
Dirksen Senate Office Bldg.,
Room 530
Washington, DC 20510
U.S. senator

The Prudential Insurance Co. Of America
Prudential Insurance Co. Bldg.
763 Broad St.
Newark, NJ 07102
Robert A. Beck,
chairman and CEO

Pryor, Alan
c/o Irving Rudd, Top Rank, Inc.
919 3rd Ave.
New York, NY 10022
Boxer

Pryor, David Hampton
Russell Senate Office Bldg.
Room 264
Washington, DC 20510
U.S. senator

Pryor, Richard
8899 Beverly Blvd.
Los Angeles, CA 90048
Actor, writer, comedian

Puente, Tito
c/o Ralph Mercado Management
1650 Broadway
New York, NY 10019
Orchestra leader, conductor

Pugh, Robert L.
U.S. Ambassador to Mauritania,
c/o U.S. State Dept.
Washington, DC 20520
U.S. ambassador to Mauritania

Purcell, Sarah
602 N. Alden Dr.
Beverly Hills, CA 90210
Television personality

Purim, Flora
c/o MPM Management
518 N. La Cienega Blvd.
Los Angeles, CA 90048
Singer

Purolator Courier Corp.
131 Morristown Rd.
Basking Ridge, NJ 07920
C. Howard Hardesty, Jr.,
president, chairman, and CEO

Puzo, Mario
c/o G. P. Putnam's Sons
200 Madison Ave.
New York, NY 10016
Author

Pyle, Denver
c/o Lew Sherrell Agency Ltd.
7060 Hollywood Blvd.
Los Angeles, CA 90028
Actor

Qaddafi, Muammar, Col.
People's Bureau
Tripoli, Libya
Leader of Lybian government

Quaid, Dennis
c/o Phil Gersh Agency
222 N. Canon Dr.
Beverly Hills, CA 90210
Actor

Quainton, Anthony Cecil Eden
Kuwait Ambassador, c/o U.S.
State Dept.
2201 C St.
NW. Washington, DC 20520
U.S. ambassador to Kuwait

Quaker Oats Co.
P.O. Box 9001
Chicago, IL 60609
*William D. Smithburg,
chairman and CEO*

Quaker State Oil Refining Corp.
255 Elm St.
Oil City, PA 16301
*Quentin E. Wood,
chairman and CEO*

Quayle, Dan
Hart Senate Office Bldg.
Room 524
Washington, DC 20510
U.S. senator

Questel, Mae
c/o Jack E. Shelby
27 E. 65th St.
New York, NY 10021
Actress

Quinn, Aidan
c/o Leading Artists, Inc.
445 N. Bedford Dr.
Beverly Hills, CA 90210
Actor

Quinn, Anthony (Anthony Rudolph Oaxaca)
9200 Sunset Blvd., Suite 1009
Los Angeles, CA 90069
Actor

Quinn, Bob
c/o Cleveland Indians
Boudreau Blvd.
Cleveland, OH 44114
Baseball team exec.

Quinn, John
P.O. Box 10
Inglewood, CA 90306
Coach, Los Angeles Kings hockey team

Quisenberry, Dan
P.O. Box 169
Kansas City, MO 64141
Baseball player

Ra, Sun (Le Sony'R Ra)
P.O. Box 7124
Chicago, IL 60607
Musician, orchestra leader

Rabb, Ellis
5000 Poplar Ave., Suite 10
Memphis, TN 38117
Actor, director, writer

Rabbit, Eddie
9229 Sunset Blvd., 9th Floor
Los Angeles, CA 90069
Singer, Songwriter

Rader, Douglas Lee
P. O. Box 1111
Arlington, TX 76010
Baseball team manager

Radio Shack
P.O. Box 17180
Fort Worth, TX 76102
B. Appel, president

Radner, Gilda
4200 Sunset Blvd., Suite 428
Los Angeles, CA 90029
Comedienne

Rae, Charlotte
9200 Sunset Blvd., Garden Suite B
Los Angeles, CA 90069
Actress

Rafelson, Bob
1400 N. Fuller Ave.
Hollywood, CA 90046
Creator of television series
The Monkees

Raffin, Deborah
12711 Ventura Blvd., Suite 250
Studio City, CA 91604
Actress

Rafkin, Alan
c/o ABC Press Relations
1330 Ave. of the Americas
New York, NY 10019
Television director

Ragu Foods, Inc.
33 Benedict Place
Greenwich, CT 06830
Charles R. Perrin, president

Raines, Tim
P.O. Box 500
Station M
Montreal, PQ HIV 3P2
Canada
Baseball player

Raitt, Bonnie
c/o Warner Brothers Records,
Inc.
3300 Warner Blvd.
Burbank, CA 91505
Singer

Raitt, John Emmet
c/o Lew Sherrell Agency Ltd.
7060 Hollywood Blvd.
Los Angeles, CA 90028
Actor, producer, director, singer

Ralston Purina Co.
Checkerboard Sq.
St. Louis, MO 63164
*William P. Stiritz,
president, chairman, and CEO*

Ramada Inns, Inc.
3838 E. Van Buren St.
Phoenix, AZ 85008
*Richard Snell,
chairman, president, and CEO*

Rampal, Jean-Pierre Louis
111 W. 57th St.
New York, NY 10019
Flutist

Ramsay, John T.
Lloyd Bldg.
700 NE. Multnomah, Suite 950
Portland, OR 97232
Basketball coach

**Randall, Tony
(Leonard Rosenberg)**
9200 Sunset Blvd., Suite 909
Los Angeles, CA 90069
Actor

Randolph, John
9255 Sunset Blvd.
Los Angeles, CA 90069
Actor

Random House, Inc.
201 E. 50th St.
New York, NY 10022
*Robert L. Bernstein,
chairman, president, and CEO*

**Rashad, Ahmad (Bobby
Moore)**
c/o NBC Sports
30 Rockefeller Plaza
New York, NY 10112
*Sportscaster, former football
player*

Rather, Dan
c/o CBS News
524 W. 57th St.
New York, NY 10019
Broadcast journalist

Ratt
P.O. Box 93519
Los Angeles, CA 90093
Heavy metal rock band

Rawlings, Lester
c/o Richard Astor
1697 Broadway
New York, NY 10019
Actor, production company exec.

Rawls, Eugina
510 E. 84th St.
New York, NY 10028
Actress

Rawls, Lou
9200 Sunset Blvd., Suite 823
Los Angeles, CA 90069
Singer

Ray, Richard
P.O. Box 558
Manvel, TX 77578
Treasure hunter

Rayburn, Gene
118 E. 25th St., 6th Floor
New York, NY 10010
Television performer

Raymond, Gene
9570 Wilshire Blvd.
Beverly Hills, CA 90212
Actor, director, producer, composer

Rayovac Corp.
101 E. Washington Ave.
Madison, WI 53703
Lionel N. Sterling, chairman

RCA Corp.
30 Rockefeller Plaza
New York, NY 10112
Robert R. Frederick, chairman and CEO

Reader's Digest Association, Inc.
Pleasantville, NY 10570
George V. Grune, Chairman and CEO. *Has highest subscription rate in the U.S.*

Reagan, Nancy
The White House
1600 Pennsylvania Ave.
Washington, DC 20500
Wife of President Ronald Reagan

Reagan, Ronald
The White House
1600 Pennsylvania Ave.
Washington, DC 20500
40th president of the United States

Reasoner, Harry
c/o CBS News
524 W. 57th St.
New York, NY 10019
Television news reporter

Reddy, Helen
10100 Santa Monica Blvd.
16th Floor
Los Angeles, CA 90067
Singer

Redford, Robert
c/o Wildwood Enterprises
100 Universal City Plaza
Universal City, CA 91608
Actor, director

Redgrave, Lynn
9200 Sunset Blvd., Suite 1009
Los Angeles, CA 90069
Actress

Redgrave, Vanessa
9000 Sunset Blvd., Suite 1200
Los Angeles, CA 90069
Actress

Reed, Jerry
45 Music Sq. W.
Nashville, TN 37203
Country music singer, composer

**Reed, Oliver
(Robert Oliver Reed)**
c/o Omega Productions
314 High St.
Dorking, Surrey, England
Actor

Reed, Rex
c/o Chicago Tribune–New York
News Syndicate, Inc.
220 E. 42nd St.
New York, NY 10017
Author, critic

**Reese, Della
(Delloreese Patricia Early)**
151 El Camino Dr.
Beverly Hills, CA 90212
Singer

Reeve, Christopher
1888 Century Park E., Suite 1400
Los Angeles, CA 90067
Actor

Rehnquist, William Hubbs
c/o Supreme Court of the
United States
Washington, DC 20543
Chief Justice, U.S. Supreme Court

Reid, Harold Wilson
P.O. Box 2703
Staunton, VA 24401
Entertainer

Reid, Kate
c/o Actor's Equity
165 W. 46th St.
New York, NY 10036
Actress

Reilly, Charles Nelson
1350 Ave. of the Americas
New York, NY 10019
Actor, director

Reiner, Carl
7950 Sunset Blvd.
Hollywood, CA 90046
*Motion picture and television
writer, director, actor*

Reiner, Rob
1888 Century Park E., Suite 1400
Los Angeles, CA 90067
Actor, writer, director

Reinking, Ann
1000 Santa Monica Blvd.
Suite 305
Los Angeles, CA 90067
Actress, dancer

Reitman, Ivan
4000 Warner Blvd.
Burbank, CA 91505
Motion picture director, producer

R.E.M.
P.O. Box 8032
Athens, GA 30603
Rock band

Remick, Lee
8899 Beverly Blvd.
Los Angeles, CA 90048
Actress

Remsen, Herbert B.
9056 Santa Monica Blvd.
Suite 206
Los Angeles, CA 90069
Actor

REO Speedwagon
1046 Carol Dr.
Los Angeles, CA 90069
Rock band

Resch, Glenn Allan
1155 Conklin St.
Farmingdale, NY 11735
Hockey player

Restless Heart
10100 Santa Monica Blvd.
16th Floor
Los Angeles, CA 90067
Country rock band

Reuther, David Louis
c/o William Morrow & Co.
105 Madison Ave.
New York, NY 10016
Children's book publisher, writer

Revlon, Inc.
767 5th Ave.
New York, NY 10022
*Michel C. Bergerac,
chairman, president, and CEO*

Reynolds, Burt
1888 Century Park E., Suite 1400
Los Angeles, CA 90067
Actor

**Reynolds, Debbie
(Mary Francis Reynolds)**
11595 La Maida
North Hollywood, CA 91601
Actress

Reynolds Metals Co.
6601 Broad Street Rd.
Richmond, VA 23233
*William O'Bourke,
president and CEO*

Rhodes, Willard
13615 Redwood Dr.
Sun City, AZ 85351
Ethnomusicologist

Rice, Donna
10100 Santa Monica Blvd.
16th Floor
Los Angeles, CA 90067
Model

Rice, James Edward
c/o Boston Red Sox
24 Yawkey Way
Boston, MA 02215
Baseball player

Rich, Charlie
8229 Rockcreek Pkwy.
Cordova, TN 38018
Country singer

Richards, Keith
"Redlands"
West Wittering
Chichester, Sussex, England
Rock guitarist, songwriter

Richie, Lionel B., Jr.
9200 Sunset Blvd., Suite 915
Los Angeles, CA 90069
Singer, songwriter

Richman, Peter Mark
15301 Ventura Blvd., Suite 345
Sherman Oaks, CA 91405
Actor, painter, writer

Rickles, Don
c/o Shefrin Co.
800 S. Robertson Blvd.
Los Angeles, CA 90035
Comedian

Ride, Sally Kristen
c/o NASA Johnson Space Center
Houston, TX 77058
First American woman in space

Riegle, Donald Wayne, Jr.
Dirksen Senate Office Bldg.,
Room 105
Washington, DC 20510
U. S. senator

Rigby, Cathy
c/o McCoy-Rigby Productions
730 E. 3rd St.
Long Beach, CA 90802
Former gymnast

Rigg, Diana
c/o London Management
235 Regent St.
London WIA 2JT England
Actress

Right to Choose
P.O. Box 33
Old Bethpage, NY 11804
Sue Bartczak, vice president and media director

Riley, Jack
10000 Santa Monica Blvd.
Suite 305
Los Angeles, CA 90067
Actor, writer

Riley, Patrick James
P.O. Box 10
Inglewood, CA 90306
Coach, Los Angeles Lakers basketball team

THE ADDRESS BOOK

Riley, Richard Wilson
P.O. Box 11450
Columbia, SC 29211
Governor of South Carolina

Rio, Frank
10100 Santa Monica Blvd.
16th Floor
Los Angeles, CA 90067
Theatrical agent

**Ritter, John
(Johnathan Southworth
Ritter)**
11777 San Vicente Blvd.
Suite 600
Los Angeles, CA 90049
Actor

Rivera, Chita
c/o Armando Rivera
91 Clinton St.
New York, NY 10002
Actress, singer, dancer

Rivers, Joan
9200 Sunset Blvd., Suite 1001
Los Angeles, CA 90069
Entertainer

Robards, Jason
c/o STE Representation Ltd.
888 7th Ave.
New York, NY 10019
Actor

Robb, Charles Spittal
Office of the Governor

State Capitol
Richmond, VA 23219
Governor of Virginia

Robbins, Harold
c/o Ernst Cane Berner & Gitlin
7 W. 51 St.
New York, NY 10019
Author

Robbins, Jerome
c/o New York City Ballet
New York State Theater
Lincoln Center
New York, NY 10023
Choregrapher, director

Robbins, Tom
c/o Phoebe Larmore
228 Main St.
Venice, CA 90291
Author

Roberts, Doris
6225 Quebec Dr.
Los Angeles, CA 90068
Actress

Roberts, Janet Louise
c/o Garon-Brooke Associates
415 Central Park W.
New York, NY 10025
Librarian, author

Roberts, Pernell
c/o Lazard Freres
One Rockefeller Plaza
New York, NY 10020
Actor

Roberts, Tanya
1446 Belfast Dr.
Los Angeles, CA 90069
Actress

**Roberts, Tony
(David Anthony Roberts)**
c/o William Morris Agency
1350 Ave. of the Americas
New York, NY 10019
Actor

Robertson, Cliff
8899 Beverly Blvd.
Los Angeles, CA 90048
Actor

Robertson, Nan
c/o New York Times
229 W. 43rd St.
New York, NY 10036
Journalist, correspondent

Robeson, William R.
15303 Ventura Blvd., 9th Floor
Sherman Oaks, CA 91403
*Executive coordinator, Premier
Luxury Liners, Inc. Provides limos
with bulletproof glass and other
safeguards*

Robinson, Earl Hawley
3937 Bledsoe Ave.
Los Angeles, CA 90066
*Conductor, composer, writer,
singer, lecturer*

Robinson, John
2327 W. Linoln Ave.

Anaheim, CA 92801
Football coach

Robinson, Smokey
c/o Michael Roshkind
6255 Sunset Blvd.
Los Angeles, CA 90028
Singer, songwriter

Robinson, Sugar Ray
1060 S. Crenshaw Blvd.
Los Angeles, CA 90019
World boxing champ

Rock Against Drugs
3575 Cahuenga Blvd. W.
Suite 204
Los Angeles, CA 90068

**Rockefeller, Blanchette
(Mrs. John D. Rockefeller)**
30 Rockefeller Plaza, Room 5600
New York, NY 10112
Organization exec.

**Rockefeller, John
Davison IV**
Dirksen Senate Office Bldg.,
Room 241
Washington, DC 20510
*U. S. senator, former governor of
West Virginia*

**Rockwell International
Corp.**
600 Grant St.
Pittsburgh, PA 15219
*Robert Anderson,
chairman and CEO*

Rodgers, William Henry
370 Chestnut Hill Ave.
Boston, MA 02146
Professional runner

Roeg, Nicholas
2 Oxford and Cambridge Mansions, Flat E
Old Marylebone Rd.
London NW1 England
Motion picture director

Roerick, William
Lost Farm
Tyringham, MA 01264
Actor, author

**Rogers, Ginger
(Virginia Katherine Mc-
Math)**
Thunderbird Country Club
Rancho Mirage, CA 92270
Dancer, actress

Rogers, John W.
c/o United Parcel Service of
America, Inc.
51 Weaver St.
Greenwich, CT 06830
*Chairman, CEO, United Parcel
Service*

Rogers, Kenny
c/o Ken Kragen Co.
1112 N. Sherbourne Dr.
Los Angeles, CA 90069
Singer

Rogers, Wayne
151 El Camino Dr.
Beverly Hills, CA 90212
Actor

Rolle, Esther
10100 Santa Monica Blvd.
16th Floor
Los Angeles, CA 90067
Actress

Rolling Stone Magazine
745 5th Ave.
New York, NY 10022
*Jann Wenner, editor and
publisher*

Rollins, Jack
c/o Rollins Joffe Morra Brezner
Productions
130 W. 57th St.
New York, NY 10019
Producer of Woody Allen films

Romero, Cesar
12115 San Vicente Blvd.
Los Angeles, CA 90049
Actor

Ronan, William John
P.O. Box 488
Glen Cove, NY 11542
Business exec.

Ronstadt, Linda
c/o Asher/Krost Management, Inc.
644 N. Doheny Dr.
Los Angeles, CA 90069
Singer

**Rooney, Andy
(Andrew Aitkin Rooney)**
51 W. 52nd St.
New York, NY 10019
*Television commentator,
columnist*

**Rooney, Mickey (Joe Yule,
Jr.)**
P.O. Box 5028
Thousand Oaks, CA 91360
Actor

Roosevelt, Selwa S.
c/o U.S. State Department
2201 C St., Room 1232
NW. Washington, DC 20520
*Chief of protocol of The United
States*

Rose, Pete
100 Riverfront Stadium
Cincinnati, OH 45202
Baseball player and manager

**Rosenberger, Walter
Emerson**
11 Woodmere Ln.
Tenafly,. NJ 07670
Percussionist

Rosenblueth, Emilio
Instituto de Ingenieria
Ciudad Universitaria
Mexico City DF 04510
Mexico
Earthquake engineer

Ross, Diana
P.O. Box 1683
New York, NY 10185
Singer, actress, fashion designer

Ross, Herbert David
151 El Camino Dr.
Beverly Hills, CA 90212
Motion picture director

Ross, Katharine
1888 Century Park E., Suite 1400
Los Angeles, CA 90067
Actress

Ross, Marion
14159 Riverside Dr.
Sherman Oaks, CA 91423
Actress

Rosser, John B.
4209 Manitou Way
Madison, WI 53711
Mathematician, rocket ballistician

Roth, David Lee
3960 Laurel Canyon Blvd.,
Number 430
Studio City, CA 91604
Rock singer

Roth, June Doris Spiewak
1057 Oakland Ct.
Teaneck, NJ 07666
Author

Roth, William V., Jr.
Hart Senate Office Bldg.
Washington, DC 20510
U.S. senator

Roto-Rooter
1400 DuBois Tower
Cincinnati, OH 45202
William R. Griffin,
president and CEO

Roundfield, Danny
Thomas
c/o Atlanta Hawks
100 Techwood Dr. NW.
Atlanta, GA 30303
Basketball player

Roundtree, Richard
9000 Sunset Blvd., Suite B
Los Angeles, CA 90069
Actor

Rowan, Carl Thomas
3251-C Sutton Place NW.
Washington, DC 20016
Columnist

Rowlands, Gena
8899 Beverly Blvd.
Los Angeles, CA 90048
Actress

Royal Crown Companies,
Inc.
41 Perimeter Center E., NE.
Atlanta, GA 30346
Donald A. McMahon, president
Makers of RC Cola

Rozelle, Pete
c/o Commissioner's Office, NFL
410 Park Ave.
New York, NY 10022
Commissioner of the National
Football League

Rubbermaid, Inc.
1147 Akron Rd.
Wooster, OH 44691
Stanley C. Gault,
chairman and CEO

Rubik, Erno
Bimbo ut 210
1026 Budapest, Hungary
Inventor of Rubik's cube and other
mind-boggling games

Rubinstein, John Arthur
1875 Century Park E., Suite 1300
Los Angeles, CA 90067
Actor, composer

Rudhyar, Dane
3635 Lupine Ave.
Palo Alto, CA 94303
Author, composer

Rudman, Warren Bruce
Hart Senate Office Bldg.
Room 530
Washington, DC 20510
U.S. senator

Runcie, Robert Alexander
Kennedy
Lambeth Palace
London SE1 9JU England
Archbishop of Canterbury

Rundgren, Todd
c/o Bearsville/Warner Brothers
Records
3300 Warner Blvd.
Burbank, CA 91505
Musician, record producer

Run-DMC
298 Elizabeth St.
New York, NY 10012
Rap group

Rush, Barbara
9744 Wilshire Blvd., Suite 206
Beverly Hills, CA 90212
Actress

Rusk, Dean
620 Hill St.
Athens, GA 30606
Educator, former secretary of state

Ruska, Dr. Ernst
Max-Eyth-Str. 20
1000 Berlin 33
Federal Republic of Germany
Inventor of the electron microscope

Russell, Jane
P.O. Box 590
Sedona, AZ 86336
Actress

Russell, Ken
8899 Beverly Blvd.
Los Angeles, CA 90048
Motion picture and theater director

Russell, Kurt Von Vogel
151 El Camino Dr.
Beverly Hills, CA 90212
Actor

Russell, Mark
2800 Wisconsin Ave.
Washington, DC 20007
Comedian

Russo, Paul
The White House
1600 Pennsylvania Ave.
Washington, DC 20500
Special assistant to the president

Rust-Oleum Corp.
11 Hawthorn Pkwy.
Vernon Hills, IL 60061
Rex Reade, president

Rutheford, John Sherman III
RR18, Box 340B
Indianapolis, IN 46234
Pro race car driver

Ryan, Nolan
P.O. Box 228
Houston, TX 77001
Baseball player

SAAB-Scania of America, Inc.
P.O. Box 697
Orange, CT 06477
Robert J. Sinclair, president

Saberhagen, Bret
P.O. Box 1969
Kansas City, MO 64141
Baseball player

Safer, Morley
c/o CBS
524 W. 57th St.
New York, NY 10019
Cohost, 60 Minutes

Safeway Stores, Inc.
201 4th St.
Oakland, CA 94660
Peter A. Magowan, chairman and CEO

Sagan, Carl Edward
Cornell University, Space Science Bldg.
Ithaca, NY 14853
Astronomer, author, educator

Sager, Carol Bayer
c/o Chapell Music
810 7th Ave.

New York, NY 10019
Lyricist, singer

Sahakian, William
c/o Suffolk University
Beacon Hill
Boston, MA 02114
Psychologist

Sahl, Mort (Morton Lyon Sahl)
c/o Harcourt Brace Jovanovich, Inc.
757 3rd Ave.
New York, NY 10017
Comedian

Saint, Eva Marie
c/o Bauman Hiller & Associates
9220 W. Sunset Blvd.
Los Angeles, CA 90069
Actress

Saint James, Susan
1888 Century Park E., Suite 1400
Los Angeles, CA 90067
Actress

St. John, Jill
9200 Sunset Blvd., Number 1009
Los Angeles, CA 90069
Actress

Saks, Michael
P.O. Box 467
Rockville Centre, NY 11571-0467
*President, Universal Autograph
Collectors Club, and editor of
The Pen and Quill*

Salazar, Alberto
c/o International Management
Group
Cuyahoga Savings Bldg.
Cleveland, OH 44114
Runner, Olympic athlete

Salk, Jonas
P.O. Box 85800
San Diego, CA 92138
Physician, scientist

Salvador, Sal
1697 Broadway
New York, NY 10019
Jazz musician, composer, educator

The Salvation Army
799 Bloomfield Ave.
Verona, NJ 07044
*Col. James Osborne, national chief
secretary*

Samrin, Heng
Office of the President
Phnom Penh, Cambodia
President of Cambodia

Samsonite Corp.
11200 E. 45th Ave.
Denver, CO 80239
Malcolm Conplish, president

Sanborn, David
151 El Camino Dr.
Beverly Hills, CA 90212
Singer, songwriter

Sandell, Richard Arnold
c/o Aurag International
16 Bramblebrook Rd.
Ardsley, NY 10502
*Investment company exec.,
economist*

Sanders, Richard
10960 Wilshire Blvd., Suite 908
Los Angeles, CA 90024
Actor

Sanders-Greenberg, Harry
125 6th St., Suite 950
Minneapolis, MN 55402
*President, Pets Are Inn, a special
inn for pets that's more luxurious
than a kennel*

Sanford, Isabel
c/o MEW Inc.
151 N. San Vicente Blvd.
Beverly Hills, CA 90211
Actress

Santana, Carlos
P.O. Box 1994
San Francisco, CA 94101
Rock guitarist

Santos, Joe
12750 Ventura Blvd., Suite 102
Studio City, CA 91604
Actor

Sanyo Electric, Inc.
1200 W. Artesia Blvd.
Compton, CA 90220
Y. Takemoto, chairman

Sara Lee Corp.
3 First National Plaza
Chicago, IL 60602
John H. Beyan, Jr.,
chairman and CEO

Sarandon, Susan Abigail
1350 Ave. of the Americas
New York, NY 10019
Actress

Sarbanes, Paul Spyros
Dirksen Senate Office Bldg.
Washington, DC 20510
U. S. senator

Sassoon, Vidal
2049 Century Park E.
Los Angeles, CA 90067
Hair stylist

Savalas, Telly Aristoteles
333 Universal City Plaza
Universal City, CA 91608
Actor

Save the Children
P.O. Box 950
Westport, CT 06881
Jane B. Levene, media coordinator

Sawyer, Diane
(L. Diane Sawyer)
c/o CBS News
524 W. 57th St.
New York, NY 10019
Cohost, 60 Minutes

Sawyer Brown
128 Volunteer Dr.
Hendersonville, TN 37075
Music group

Sax, Steve
Dodger Stadium
1000 Elysian Park Ave.
Los Angeles, CA 90012
Baseball player

Sayer, Leo
1801 Century Park E., Suite 1132
Los Angeles, CA 90067
Musician, singer

Scaggs, Boz
(William Royce Scaggs)
c/o CBS Records
51 W. 52nd St.
New York, NY 10019
Musician, singer, songwriter

Scarborough, Charles
Bishop III
30 Rockefeller Plaza
New York, NY 10112
Broadcast journalist, author

Scarbrough, W. Carl
1910 Air Lane Dr.
Nashville, TN 37210
*President, United Furniture
Workers of America AFL-CIO*

Scarwid, Diana
1888 Century Park E., Suite 1400
Los Angeles, CA 90067
Actress

Scheider, Roy Richard
11 E. 73rd St., Number 2B
New York, NY 10021
Actor

Schell, Maximilian
8899 Beverly Blvd.
Los Angeles, CA 90048
Actor

Schenkel, Chris
c/o ABC Sports
1330 Ave. of the Americas
New York, NY 10019
Sportscaster

Schickel, Richard
311 E. 83rd St.
New York, NY 10028
Writer

Schieffer, Bob
c/o CBS News
51 W. 52nd St.
New York, NY 10019
Broadcast journalist

Schiller, Robert Archille
Box 900
Beverly Hills, CA 90213
Television producer and writer

Schlafly, Phyllis
68 Fairmount St.
Alton, IL 62002
Author, lawyer

Schmidt, Michael
P.O. Box 2575
Philadelphia, PA 19101
Baseball player

Schmitt, Harrison Hagan
Route 8, Box 226
Silver City, NM 88061
Astronaut, former U.S. senator

Schneider, Mitchell R.
8730 Sunset Blvd., 6th Floor
Los Angeles, CA 90069
Music publicist

Schopf, James William
c/o Department of Earth and
Space Sciences
Los Angeles, CA 90024
Paleobiologist

Schramm, Texas E.
6116 N. Central Expressway
Dallas, TX 75206
Football club official

Schulian, John Neilsen
401 N. Wabash Ave.
Chicago, IL 60611
Sports columnist

Schuller, Gunther
167 Dudley Rd.
Newton Center, MA 02159
Composer

Schulz, Charles Monroe
c/o United Features Syndicate
200 Park Ave.
New York, NY 10166
Cartoonist, creator of "Peanuts"

Schultz, Michael
c/o Eisenbach Green Duchow
760 N. La Cienega Blvd.
Los Angeles, CA 90069
Stage and motion picture director

Schwartz, Bermuda
6617 Orange St., Number 201
Los Angeles, CA 90048
Drummer for the "Wierd Al Yan-kovic" Band

Schwarzenegger, Arnold Alois
c/o Oak Productions
321 Hampton Dr.
Venice, CA 90291
Actor, author, businessman, former body building champ

Schweppes, U.S.A.
High Ridge Park
Stamford, CT 06905
John C. Carson, president

Schwinden, Ted
Office of Governor
State Capitol
Helena, MT 59620
Governor of Montana

Scorsese, Martin
c/o Jay Julien & Associates
1501 Broadway
New York, NY 10036
Motion picture writer and director

Scott, David R.
858 W. Jackson St., Suite 202
Lancaster, CA 93534
Former astronaut, engineering exec.

Scott, George Campbell
c/o Jane Deacy Agency, Inc.
300 E. 7th St.
New York, NY 10021
Actor

Scott, Henry L.
34 Smith St.
Charleston, SC 29401
Concert pianist, humorist

Scott, Willard Herman
30 Rockefeller Plaza, Room 789
New York, NY 10112
Radio and television performer

Scotti, Vito
c/o Frank Campana
20121 Ventura Blvd.
Woodland Hills, CA 91364
Actor

Scott Paper Co.
Scott Plaza
Philadelphia, PA 19113
*Philip E. Lippincott,
president, chairman, and CEO*

Scrimshaw, Nevin Stewart
MIT. 18 Vassar St.
Room 20A-201
Cambridge, MA 02139
*Food science educator and
consultant*

Scully, Vincent Edward
c/o NBC Sports
30 Rockefeller Plaza
New York, NY 10112
Sportscaster

Seaborg, Glenn Theodore
University of California at
Berkeley
Lawrence Berkeley Lab
Berkeley, CA 94720
Chemistry specialist, educator

The Seagram Co., Ltd.
375 Park Ave.
New York, NY 10152
*Edgar M. Bronfman,
chairman and CEO*

**The Search for Tomorrow
Fan Club**
R.R. Number 6, Box 165
Lake Dr.
Mahopac, NY 10541
Marylou Bondi, president

Sears, Roebuck, and Co.
Sears Tower
Chicago, IL 60606
*Edward A. Brennan,
chairman and CEO*

Seaver, Tom
c/o Chicago White Sox, Comis-
key
Park
Dan Ryan at 35th St.
Chicago, IL 60616
Baseball player

Security Pacific Corp.
333 S. Hope St.
Los Angeles, CA 90071
George F. Moody, president

Sedaka, Neil
1370 Ave. of the Americas
New York, NY 10019
Singer, songwriter

Seeger, Pete
c/o Harold Leventhal
250 W. 57th St.
New York, NY 10107
Folk singer, composer

See's Candy Shops, Inc.
210 El Camino Real
San Francisco, CA 94080
Warren E. Buffett, chairman

Segal, George
1888 Century Park E., Suite 1400
Los Angeles, CA 90067
Actor

Seger, Bob
567 Purdy St.
Birmingham, MI 48009
Rock singer, songwriter, musician

Seka
840 N. Michigan Ave., Suite 408
Chicago, IL 60611
Porno movie queen

Selleck, Tom
9200 Sunset Blvd., Suite 1009
Los Angeles, CA 91608
Actor

Selmon, Lee Roy
c/o Tampa Bay Buccaneers
One Buccaneer Pl.
Tampa, FL 33607
Football player

Selzer, Milton
9200 Sunset Blvd., Suite 909
Los Angeles, CA 90069
Actor

Serafin, Barry
c/o ABC News
1717 DeSales St.
Washington, DC 20036
ABC Television news correspondent

Serral, Frederick Amos
c/o Austin Co., Inc.
C. Hall and Cutler Sts.
Greenville, TN 37743
Tobacconist

The Seven-Up Co.
121 S. Meramec
St. Louis, MO 63105
Edward W. Frantel, president and CEO

**Severinsen, Doc
(Carl H. Severinsen)**
c/o NBC Press Dept.
30 Rockefeller Plaza
New York, NY 10112
Musical director, The Tonight Show Starring Johnny Carson

Sexaholics Anonymous
P.O. Box 300
Simi Valley, CA 93062
Attn: General information

Seymour, Jane
9200 Sunset Blvd., Suite 1009
Los Angeles, CA 90069
Actress

Shackelford, Ted
c/o Le Mond/Zetter Inc.
526 N. La Cienega Blvd.
Los Angeles, CA 90048
Actor

Shalit, Gene
c/o NBC News
30 Rockefeller Plaza
New York, NY 10112
Commentator, The Today Show

Shannon, James A.
8302 SW. Homewood St.
Portland, OR 97255
Medical investigator

Sharif, Omar
151 El Camino Dr.
Beverly Hills, CA 90212
Actor

Sharon, Dagney
P.O. Box 224
Long Beach, CA 90801
Producer

Shatner, William
151 El Camino Dr.
Beverly Hills, CA 90212
Actor

Shaw, Artie
2127 W. Palos Ct.
Newbury Park, CA 91320
Musician, writer

Shaw, Harold
c/o Shaw Concerts Inc.
1995 Broadway
New York, NY 10023
Impresario

Shaw, Woody Herman
c/o Willard Alexander, Inc.
660 Madison Ave.
New York, NY 10021
Jazz trumpeter, composer

Shearing, George
10100 Santa Monica Blvd.
16th Floor
Los Angeles, CA 90067
Pianist, composer

Shearson Lehman Brothers, Inc.
600 Montgomery St.
San Francisco, CA 94111
Peter A. Cohen, president and CEO

Sheehan, David
3000 W. Alameda, Room 2201
Burbank, CA 91505
Entertainment critic

Sheen, Martin (Ramon Estevez)
c/o Special Artists Agency
8730 Sunset Blvd.
Los Angeles, CA 90069
Actor

Sheffield, William Jennings
P.O. Box A
Juneau, AK 99811
Governor of Alaska

Sheila E. (Sheila Escavedo)
P.O. Box 2739
Oakland, CA 94602
Percussionist, singer

Sheldon, Sidney
c/o William Morrow & Co. Press Relations
105 Madison Ave.
New York, NY 10016
Author

Shelesnyak, Moses Chaim
674 Chalk Hill Rd.
Solvang, CA 93463
Biodynamicist

THE ADDRESS BOOK

Shelley, Carole Augusta
c/o Lionel Larner
850 7th Ave.
New York, NY 10019

Shell Oil Co.
One Shell Plaza
Houston, TX 77001
John F. Boocout,
president and CEO

Shelton, Reid
1650 Broadway, Suite 406
New York, NY 10019
Actor

Shepard, Jean
P.O. Box 809
Goodlettsville, TN 37072
Country singer

**Shepard, Sam
(Samuel Shepard Rogers)**
c/o Lois Berman Little Theater
Bldg.
240 W. 44th St.
New York, NY 10036
Playwright, actor

Shepherd, Cybill
15301 Ventura Blvd., Suite 345
Sherman Oaks, CA 91403
Actress

The Sheraton Co.
60 State St.
Boston, MA 02109
John Kapioltas,
president, chairman, and CEO

Sherr, Lynn
c/o ABC News
1926 Broadway
New York, NY 10023
ABC News national corres-
pondent

Shields, Brooke
P.O. Box 147
Harrington Park, NJ 07640
Actress, model

Shire, Talia Rose
1888 Century Park E., Suite 1400
Los Angeles, CA 90067
Actress

**Shlaudeman, Harry
Walter**
2201 C St., Room 7810
NW. Washington, DC 20520
Special ambassador to Central
America

**Shoemaker, Willie
(William Lee Shoemaker)**
315 S. Beverly Dr., Suite 216
Beverly Hills, CA 90212
Jockey

**Shore, Dinah (Frances
Rose Shore)**
10100 Santa Monica Blvd.
16th Floor
Los Angeles, CA 90067
Singer, television talk show
hostess

**Short, Bobby
(Robert Waltrip Short)**
c/o Betty Lee Hunt Associates
1501 Broadway
New York, NY 10036
Entertainer, author

Shorter, Frank L.
2400 Central Ave., Suite One
Boulder, CO 80301
*Sportscaster, lawyer, marathon
runner*

Shorter, Wayne
c/o Brighton Agency
9615 Brighton Way
Beverly Hills, CA 90201
Musician

**Shriver, Eunice Mary
Kennedy**
(Mrs. Robert Sargent Shriver, Jr.)
1350 New York Ave., Suite 500
Washington, DC 20005
Civic worker

**Shriver, Maria Owings
(Mrs. Arnold Schwarze-
negger)**
KNBC
3000 W. Alameda Ave.
Burbank, CA 91523
Anchor person

Shriver, Pamela Howard
c/o Pro-Serve, Inc.
888 17th St. NW.
Washington, DC 20006
Tennis player

Shula, Don
c/o Miami Dolphins
3550 Biscayne Blvd.
Miami, FL 33137
Football coach

Shultz, George Pratt
c/o U.S. Dept. of State
2201 C St.
NW. Washington, DC 20520
*Secretary of state for Reagan
administration*

Shutt, Stephen John
2313 Saint Catherine St.
W. Montreal PQ H3H IN2
Canada
Hockey player

Sidney, Sylvia
c/o John Springer
155 E. 55th St.
New York, NY 10022
Actress

Sierra Club
530 Bush St.
San Francisco, CA 94108
*Michael McCloskey, executive
director*

Sikma, Jack
c/o Seattle Supersonics
419 Occidental Ave.
Seattle, WA 98104
Basketball player

Sikora, Stephen
P.O. Box 6218
Albany, CA 94706
Editor, The Letter Exchange, a publication that allows folks with similar interests to exchange correspondence

Sills, Beverly
New York City Opera
c/o New York City State Theater
Lincoln Center
New York, NY 10023
Coloratura soprano, opera company director

Silverman, Fred
c/o MGM
10202 W. Washington Blvd.
Culver City, CA 90230
Broadcasting exec.

Silvers, Phil
c/o Contemporary Artists Ltd.
132 Lasky Dr.
Beverly Hills, CA 90212
Actor

Silverstein, Shel
c/o Harper & Row Publishers, Inc.
10 E. 53rd St.
New York, NY 10022
Author, cartoonist, composer, folksinger

Simmons, Jean
c/o Morgan Maree
6363 Wilshire Blvd.
Los Angeles, CA 90048
Actress

Simmons, Richard Milton Teagle
c/o Anthony Asylum
9306 Santa Monica Blvd.
Beverly Hills, CA 90210
Physical fitness specialist, television personality

Simmons, Ted
P.O. Box 4064
Atlanta, GA 30302
Baseball player

Simon, Carly
c/o Champion Entertainment
130 W. 57th St., Suite 12B
New York, NY 10019
Singer, songwriter

Simon, Neil
c/o Dramatists Guild
234 W. 44th St.
New York, NY 10036
Playwright, television writer

Simon, Paul
1619 Broadway, Suite 500
New York, NY 10019
Singer, songwriter

Simon & Schuster, Inc.
1230 Ave. of the Americas
New York, NY 10020
Richard E. Snyder, chairman of the board, president

Simply Red
c/o Burton Management
250 W. 57th St., Suite 1502
New York, NY 10107
Pop music group

Simpson, Alan K.
Dirksen Senate Office Bldg.,
Room 261
Washington, DC 20510
U.S. senator

Simpson, John Richard
c/o U.S. Secret Service
1800 G. St.
NW. Washington, DC 20223
Director, U.S. Secret Service;
president, INTERPOL

Simpson, O. J.
(Orenthal James Simpson)
c/o ABC Sports
1330 Ave. of the Americas
New York, NY 10019
Former football player, actor,
sports commentator

Sinatra, Frank
(Francis Albert Sinatra)
c/o Sinatra Enterprises
1041 N. Formosa Ave.
Hollywood, CA 90046
Singer, actor

Sinatra, Nancy
160 Apple Court
Luling, CA 70070
Singer, actress

Singletary, Michael
55 E. Jackson, Suite 1200
Chicago, IL 60604
Football player

Sinner, George Albert
Governor's Office, State Capitol
Bismarck, ND 58505
Governor of North Dakota,
farmer

Sirhan, Sirhan
Soledad State Prison
Soledad, CA 93960
Convicted assassin of Robert F.
Kennedy

Siskel, Gene
(Eugene Kal Siskel)
c/o Chicago Tribune
435 N. Michigan Ave.
Chicago, IL 60611
Film critic

Skaggs, Ricky
P.O. Box 150871
Nashville, TN 37215
Country musician

Skinner, Burrhus Frederic
13 Old Dee Rd.
Cambridge, MA 02138
Psychologist, educator

Slaughter, Frank G.
P.O. Box 14
Ortega Station
Jackson, FL 32210
Author, physician

Slayton, Donald Kent
7015 Gulf Freeway, Suite 140
Houston, TX 77087
*One of the original Mercury
astronauts*

Smalley, Eugene Byron
Dept. of Plant Pathology
1630 Linden Dr.
Madison, WI 53706
*Plant pathology educator,
mycologist*

Smith, Donna
P.O. Box 22253
Milwaukee, OR 97222
*President, Pro Creations Mater-
nity Leasewear. Company leases
maternity clothes designed for
professionals*

Smith, Hal
P.O. Box 3184
Santa Monica, CA 90403
Actor

Smith, Homer Duggibs, Jr.
c/o NATO
Boulevard Leopold III
EVERE 1110 Brussels, Belgium
International logistician

Smith, Jaclyn
1888 Century Park E., Suite 1400
Los Angeles, CA 90067
Actress

Smith, Maggie
c/o ICM Ltd.
388 Oxford St.
London WIN 9HE, England
Actress

Smith, Robert James
301 Henrietta St.
Kalamazoo, MI 49001
Immunopharmacologist

Smith, Stanley Roger
888 17th St. NW., Suite 1200
Washington, DC 20006
Tennis player

Smith, William French
c/o Gibson, Dunn, & Crutcher
333 S. Grand Ave.
Los Angeles, CA 90071
*Lawyer, former U.S. attorney
general*

Smith & Wesson
2100 Roosevelt Ave.
Springfield, MA 01102
L. J. Deters, president and CEO

Smits, Theodore Richard
601 E. 20th St.
New York, NY 10010
Newspaper publicist

Smokers Anonymous
P.O. Box 25335
West Los Angeles, CA 90025
*Organization for people who can't
quit smoking*

The Smothers Brothers, Dick, Tom
c/o Ken Kragen
1112 Sherbourne
Los Angeles, CA 90069
Actors, singers, comedians

Smucker's (J. M. Smucker Co.)
Strawberry Lane
Orrville, OH 44667
Paul H. Smucker, chairman and CEO

Smythe, Reggie
Whitegates
96 Caledonian Rd.
Hartlepool Cleveland, England
Cartoonist, creator of "Andy Capp"

Snap-On Tools Corp.
2801 80th St.
Kenosha, WI 53140
William B. Rayburn, president, chairman, and CEO

Snead, Jesse Carlyle
Box 12458
Palm Beach Gardens, FL 33480
Golfer

Snead, Sam
Box 777
Hot Springs, VA 24445
Golfer

Sneva, Thomas
3301 E. Valley Vista
Paradise, AZ 85253
Race car driver

Snow, Phoebe
c/o TWM Management
641 Lexington Ave.
New York, NY 10022
Singer, songwriter, musician

Soble, Ronald Norman
13455 Ventura Blvd., Suite 315
Sherman Oaks, CA 91423
Actor

Society of Dirty Old Men
P.O. Box 18202
Indianapolis, IN 46218
D. M. Butler

Solomon, Harold Charles
c/o International Management Group
One Erieview Plaza
Cleveland, OH 44114
Tennis player

Somers, Suzanne
8730 Sunset Blvd., 6th Floor
Los Angeles, CA 90069
Actress, singer, entertainer

Sommer, Elke (Elke Schletz)
c/o The Light Co.
113 N. Robertson Rd.
Los Angeles, CA 90048
Actress

Sony Corp.
7-35, Kitashinagwa
6-Chrome, Shinagawa-Ku
Tokyo, Japan
Masaru Ibuka, honorable chairman

Sorvino, Paul
c/o Charter Management
9000 Sunset Blvd.
Los Angeles, CA 90069
Actor

Soule, Gardner Bosworth
517 W. 113th St.
New York, NY 10025
Author

**Southern Pacific
Transportation Co.**
One Market Plaza
San Francisco, CA 94105
*Denman K. McNear,
president, chairman, and CEO*

**Spacek, Sissy
(Mary Elizabeth Spacek)**
1888 Century Park E., Suite 1400
Los Angeles, CA 90067
Actress

Spago (Restaurant)
8795 Sunset Blvd.
Los Angeles, CA 90069
Wolfgang Puck, master chef

Spano, Joseph
c/o Smith-Freedman & Associates
123 N. San Vicente Blvd.
Beverly Hills, CA 90211
Actor

Specter, Arlen
Hart Senate Office Bldg.
Room 331
Washington, DC 20510
U.S. senator

**Spector, Johanna
Lichtenberg**
3080 Broadway
New York, NY 10027
Ethnomusicology educator

Spector, Phil
P.O. Box 69529
Los Angeles, CA 90069
Record producer

Spelling, Aaron
1041 N. Formosa Ave.
Los Angeles, CA 90046
Producer, writer

Spielberg, Steven
c/o Amblin Entertainment
100 Universal Plaza, Bldg.
Number 477
Universal City, CA 91608
*Motion picture and television
writer, director, producer*

**Spillane, Mickey
(Frank Morrison)**
c/o Mysterious Press
129 W. 56th St.
New York, NY 10019
Author

Spinks, Michael
c/o Butch Lewis
250 W. 57th St.
New York, NY 10107
Heavyweight boxing champion

Springsteen, Bruce
136 E. 57th St., Suite 1202
New York, NY 10022
Rock singer, songwriter, guitarist

The Spruce Goose
P.O. Box 8
Pier J
Long Beach, CA 90801
Darlene D. Lynch

Spyro Gyra
278 Haverstraw Rd.
Suffern, NY 10190
Jazz group

Squirt & Co.
777 Brooks Ave.
Holland, MI 49423
*James F. Brooks,
chairman and CEO*

Stabler, Kenny
Box 382
Selma, AL 36701
Football player

Stack, Robert Langford
c/o Camden Artists
409 N. Camden Dr.
Beverly Hills, CA 90210
Actor

Stafford, Robert Theodore
Hart Senate Office Bldg.
Washington, DC 20510
U.S. senator

Stahl, Lesley
c/o CBS News
51 W. 52nd St.
New York, NY 10019
Journalist

Stahr, Elvis Jacob, Jr.
1815 H St., Suite 600
NW. Washington, DC 20006
Lawyer, conservationist, educator

Stallone, Sylvester Enzio
1888 Century Park E., Suite 1400
Los Angeles, CA 90067
*Actor, writer, producer, director,
novelist*

Standard Brands Paint Co.
4300 W. 190th St.
Torrance, CA 90509
*Stuart D. Buchalter,
chairman and CEO*

Standard Oil Co.
200 Public Sq.
Cleveland, OH 44114
R. B. Horton, chairman and CEO

Stanley, Ralph
P.O. Box 191
Floyd, VA 24012
Bluegrass musician

Stanton, Roger
17820 E. Warren St.
Detroit, MI 48224
Editor, sports broadcaster,
publisher

Stanwyck, Barbara
(Ruby Stevens)
c/o A. Morgan Maree &
Associates, Inc.
6363 Wilshire Blvd.
Los Angeles, CA 90048
Actress

Stapleton, Jean
c/o Bauman Hiller & Strain
9220 Sunset Blvd.
Los Angeles, CA 90069
Actress

Stapleton, Maureen
8899 Beverly Blvd.
Los Angeles, CA 90048
Actress

Star-Kist Foods, Inc.
582 Tuna St.
Terminal Island, CA 90731
Joseph J. Bogdanovich, chairman

Starr, Bart
c/o Green Bay Packers
1265 Lombardi Ave.
Green Bay, WI 54304
Football coach

Starr, Ringo (Richard
Starkey)
c/o Boardwalk Records
9884 Santa Monica Blvd.
Beverly Hills, CA 90212
Musician, actor, former member
of the Beatles

Starship
1319 Bridgeway
Sausalito, CA 94965
Pop music band

The Statler Brothers
P.O. Box 2703
Staunton, VA 24401
Country music group

Staubach, Roger Thomas
c/o The Staubach Co.
6750 LBJ Freeway
Dallas, TX 75240
Former football player, real estate
exec.

Stauffer, Sarah Ann
Lime Spring Farm
Rohrerstown, PA 17571
Former member of Republican
National Committee

Steenburgen, Mary
8899 Beverly Blvd.
Los Angeles, CA 90048
Actress

Stefano, Joseph
10216 Cielo Dr.
Beverly Hills, CA 90210
Author, television producer

Steiger, Rod
1888 Century Park E., Suite 1400
Los Angeles, CA 90067
Actor

Stein, Joseph
250 W. 57th St.
New York, NY 10019
Playwright

Steinberg, David
151 El Camino Dr.
Beverly Hills, CA 90212
Comedian, actor

Steinem, Gloria
c/o Ms. Magazine
119 W. 40th St.
New York, NY 10018
Writer, editor, lecturer

Stennis, John Cornelius
Russell Senate Office Bldg.
Room 205
Washington, DC 20510
U.S. senator

Stephens, Woody
98 Scherer Blvd.
Franklin Square, NY 11010
*Champion race horse trainer,
breeder*

Stephenson, Skip
8380 Melrose Ave., Number 310
Los Angeles, CA 90069
Comedian

Stern, Isaac
c/o International Creative
Management
40 W. 57th St.
New York, NY 10019
Violinist

Stern, Madeleine Bettins
Rostenberg and Stern
40 E. 88th St.
New York, NY 10028
Rare books dealer, author

Stevens, Andrew
2049 Century Park E., Suite 3700
Los Angeles, CA 90067
Actor

Stevens, Connie
1888 Century Park E., Suite 1400
Los Angeles, CA 90067
Actress, singer

Stevens, Craig
c/o Contemporary Artists Ltd.
132 Lasky Dr.
Beverly Hills, CA 90212
Actor

Stevens, John Paul
c/o U.S. Supreme Court
One 1st St.
NE. Washington, DC 20543
*Associate justice, U.S. Supreme
Court*

Stevens, Theodore Fulton
Russell Senate Office Bldg.
Washington, DC 20510
U. S. senator

Stevenson, Parker
9200 Sunset Blvd., Suite 1009
Los Angeles, CA 90069
Actor

Stewart, Jimmy
(James Maitland Stewart)
8899 Beverly Blvd.
Los Angeles, CA 90048
Actor

Stewart, Paul
c/o Gursey Schneider
1900 Ave. of the Stars
Century City, CA 90067
Actor, producer, director

Stewart, Rod
(Roderick David Stewart)
151 El Camino Dr.
Beverly Hills, CA 90212
Rock singer

Stigwood, Robert
c/o Robert Stigwood Organization, Inc.
1775 Broadway
New York, NY 10019
Theater, motion picture, television, and record producer

Stiller, Jerry
8500 Wilshire Blvd., Suite 506
Beverly Hills, CA 90211
Actor

Sting (Gordon Mathew Sumner)
250 E. 57th St., Suite 603
New York, NY 10107
Musician, songwriter, actor

Stockman, Dave
32373 Tres Lagos
Mentone, CA 92359
Pro golfer

Stockman, David
c/o Salomon Brothers
One New York Plaza
New York, NY 10004
Former government official, financier

Stockton, Dick
c/o CBS Sports
51 W. 52nd St.
New York, NY 10019
Sports broadcaster

Stoddard, Brandon
c/o ABC Motion Pictures
2040 Ave. of the Stars, 5th Floor
Los Angeles, CA 90067
President, ABC Motion Pictures

Stone, Ezra Chaim
c/o Georgia Gilly Agency
8721 Sunset Blvd.
Los Angeles, CA 90069
Producer, director, actor, writer, farmer

Stone, Milan
87 S. High St., URWA Bldg.
Akron, OH 44308
President, United Rubber, Linoleum, and Plastic Workers of America Union

Stone, Sharon
1888 Century Park E., Suite 1400
Los Angeles, CA 90067
Actress

Stotz, Carl
2015 Wheatland Ave.
Williamsport, PA 17701
Founder of Little League baseball

Stouffer Foods
57550 Harper Rd.
Solon, OH 44139
Robert McGuigan, president

STP Corp.
5300 Brokem Sound Blvd. NW.
Boca Raton, FL 33431
Leo J. LeClair, president and CEO

Stram, Hank Louis
c/o CBS Sports
51 W. 52nd St.
New York, NY 10019
Football coach, television commentator

Strasberg, Susan
c/o Joyce Star Inc.
9056 Santa Monica Blvd.
Los Angeles, CA 90069
Actress

Strauss, Peter
8899 Beverly Blvd.
Los Angeles, CA 90048
Actor

Straw Hat Pizza
6400 Village Pkwy.
Dublin, CA 94568
Everett Jefferson, president

**Streep, Meryl
(Mary Louise Streep)**
c/o International Creative Management
40 W. 57th St.
New York, NY 10019
Actress

Streisand, Barbra Joan
1040 N. Las Palmas, Bldg. 17
Los Angeles, CA 90038
Singer, actress

The Stroh Brewery Co.
100 River Pl.
Detroit, MI 48207
Peter W. Stroh, chairman

Struthers, Sally
151 El Camino Dr.
Beverly Hills, CA 90212
Actress

Stryper
P.O. Box 1045
Cyprus, CA 90630
Christian heavy metal band

Stuart, Joseph
c/o ABC TV
1330 Ave. of the Americas
New York, NY 10019
Television producer, director

Student Loan Marketing Association
1050 Thomas Jefferson St. NW.
Washington, DC 20007
*Edward A. Fox,
president and CEO*

Styne, Jule
237 W. 51st St.
New York, NY 10019
Composer, producer

Suarez, Xavier Louis
Office of Mayor
3500 Pan American Dr.
Miami, FL 33133
Mayor of Miami, lawyer

Subaru of America, Inc.
7040 Central Highway
Pennsauken, NJ 08109
*Harvey H. Lamm,
president and CEO*

Sullivan, Susan
211 Beverly Dr., Suite 201
Beverly Hills, CA 90212
Actress

Sullivan, William Hallisey, Jr.

c/o Sullivan Stadium
Route One
Foxboro, MA 02035
Football team exec., oil company exec.

Summer, Donna (La Donna Andrea Gaines)
c/o Munao Management
1224 N. Vine St.
Los Angeles, CA 90038
Singer, songwriter, actress

Summerall, Pat (George Summerall)
c/o CBS Sports
51 W. 52nd St.
New York, NY 10019
Sportscaster

Sunkist Growers, Inc.
P.O. Box 7888
Van Nuys, CA 91409
J. V. Newman, chairman

Sununu, John H.
Office of Governor
State House
Concord, NH 03301
Governor of New Hampshire

Survivor
c/o International Creative Management
40 W. 57th St.
New York, NY 10019
Pop music group

Susskind, David Howard
c/o The Susskind Co.
650 5th Ave.
New York, NY 10019
Television, motion picture, and theater producer

Sutherland, Donald
1888 Century Park E., Suite 1400
Los Angeles, CA 90067
Actor

Sutter, Howard
250 Stadium Plaza
St. Louis, MO 63102
Baseball player

Sutton, Don
1000 Elysian Park Ave.
Los Angeles, CA 90012
Baseball player

Svenson, Bo
9220 Sunset Blvd., Garden Suite B
Los Angeles, CA 90069
Actor

Swann, Lynn Curtis
300 Stadium Circle
Pittsburgh, PA 15212
Former football player, sportscaster

Swayze, John Cameron
491 Riversville Rd.
Greenwich, CT 06830
News commentator

Swayze, Patrick
c/o Joseph Heldfond & Rix
1717 N. Highland Ave.
Hollywood, CA 90028
Actor

Swit, Loretta
151 El Camino Dr.
Beverly Hills, CA 90212
Actress

Symms, Steven Douglas
Hart Senate Office Bldg.
Room 509
Washington, DC 20510
U.S. senator

Talking Heads
1775 Broadway, 7th Floor
New York, NY 10019
Pop music group

Tandy, Jessica
62-23 Carlton St.
Rego Park, NY 11374
Actress

Target Stores
P.O. Box 1392
Minneapolis, MN 55440
*Bruce G. Allbright,
chairman and CEO*

Tarkenton, Francis Asbury
3340 Peachtree Rd. NE, Suite 444
Atlanta, GA 30326
*Former football player, sports-
caster, management consultant*

Tartikoff, Brandon
c/o NBC Television Network
3000 W. Alameda Blvd.
Burbank, CA 91523
President, NBC Entertainment

**Tayback, Vic
(Victor Tabback)**
1633 Vista Del Mar, Suite 307
Beverly Hills, CA 90211
Actor

Taylor, A. Starke
Office of Mayor
2014 Main St.
Dallas, TX 75201
Mayor of Dallas

Taylor, Andy
9200 Sunset Blvd, Suite 415
Los Angeles, CA 90069
Rock guitarist, singer, songwriter

Taylor, Donald D.
24860 Lake Wohlford Ct.
Escondido, CA 92027
Technical writer, photographer

Taylor, Elizabeth
315 E. 72nd St.
New York, NY 10021
Actress

Taylor, James Vernon
c/o Peter Asher Management
644 N. Doheny Dr.
Los Angeles, CA 90069
Musician, singer, songwriter

Taylor, Lawrence
c/o New York Giants, Giant
Stadium
East Rutherford, NJ 07073
Football player

Taylor, Paul
c/o Paul Taylor Dance Co.
550 Broadway
New York, NY 10012
Artistic director, choreographer,
Paul Taylor Dance Co.

Taylor, Rip
1608 Sombrero Dr.
Las Vegas, NV 89109
Comedian

Taylor, Rod
c/o Contemporary Artists Ltd.
132 Lasky Dr.
Beverly Hills, CA 90212
Actor, producer

Teal, Gordon Kidd
5222 Park Ln.
Dallas, TX 75220
Physical scientist

Teledyne, Inc.
1901 Ave. of the Stars
Los Angeles, CA 90067
Henry E. Singleton,
chairman and CEO

Tennant, Victoria
1888 Century Park E., Suite 1400
Los Angeles, CA 90067
Actress

Tenneco, Inc.
Tenneco Bldg.
Houston, TX 77002
J. L. Ketelsen, chairman and CEO

Tenneco Automotive
108 Wilmot Rd.
Deerfield, IL 60015
James K. Ashford,
president and CEO

Teresa, Mother
Mission of Charity
Calcutta, India
Missionary, Nobel Prize winner

Terkel, Studs Louis
500 N. Michigan Ave.
Chicago, IL 60656
Interviewer, author

Terres, John Kenneth
225 Glen Rd.
Woodcliff Lake, NJ 07675
Natuarlist, author, editor

Tesich, Steve
c/o International Creative
Management
40 W. 57th St.
New York, NY 10019
Author

Tewes, Lauren
10509 Cushdon Ave.
Los Angeles, CA 90064
Actress

Texaco, Inc.
2000 Westchester Ave.
White Plains, NY 10650
John K. McKinley,
chairman and CEO

Texas Air Corp.
333 Clay St.
Houston, TX 77002
F. A. Lorenzo,
president and CEO

Texas Instruments, Inc.
P.O. Box 225474
Dallas, TX 75265
Jerry R. Junkins,
president and CEO

Tharp, Twyla
c/o Twyla Tharp Dance
Foundation
38 Walker St.
New York, NY 10013
Dancer, choreographer

Thatcher, Margret
10 Downing St.
London SW1 England
Prime minister of England

Theismann, Joseph Robert
P.O. Box 17247
Dulles International Airport
Washington, DC 20041
Football player

Theodosius (Theodore Lazor)
P.O. Box 675, Route 25A
Syosset, NY 11791
Archbishop of Washington and
metropolitan of all America and
Canada, Orthodox Church in
America

.38 Special
850 7th Ave., Suite 1105
New York, NY 10019
Rock band

Thomas, B. J. (Billy Joe Thomas)
c/o Jim Halsey, Inc.
3225 S. Norwood
Tulsa, OK 74135
Singer

Thomas, Betty
c/o NBC Press Dept.
30 Rockefeller Plaza
New York, NY 10112
Actress

Thomas, Danny (Amos Jacobs)
c/o St. Jude Children's Hospital
332 N. Lauderdale
Memphis, TN 38105
Entertainer

Thomas, Isiah Lord
c/o Detroit Pistons, Pontiac
Silverdome
1200 Featherstone
Pontiac, MI 48057
Basketball player

Thomas, Lewis
c/o Memorial-Sloan Kettering
Cancer Center
1275 York Ave.
New York, NY 10021
Physician, educator, author

Thomas, Lowell, Jr.
7022 Tanaina Dr.
Anchorage, AK 99502
*Former lieutenant governor of
Alaska, former state senator,
author, lecturer*

Thomas, Marlo
1888 Century Park E., Suite 1400
Los Angeles, CA 90067
Actress

Thomas, Richard
c/o John Springer Associates
155 E. 55th St.
New York, NY 10022
Actor

Thomas, W. Dennis
c/o White House Staff
1600 Pennsylvania Ave.
Washington, DC 20500
Assistant to President Reagan

Thom Mc An Shoe Co.
67 Milbrook St.
Worcester, MA 01606
Larry A. McVey, president

Thompson, Daley
One Church Row
Wandsworth Plain
London SW18 England
Olympic decathalon champion

Thompson, Dave
4781 E. Powell
Las Vegas, NV 89121
Las Vegas football handicapper

Thompson, James Robert
c/o Office of Governor
State House
Springfield, IL 62706
Governor of Illinois

Thompson, Lea
P.O. Box 16894
Baltimore, MD 21206
Actress

**Thompson, (Richard)
Ernest**
9000 Sunset Blvd., Suite 1115
Los Angeles, CA 90069
Writer, actor

Thompson, Sada Carolyn
250 W. 57th St., Suite 803
New York, NY 10107
Actress

Thompson Twins
10100 Santa Monica Blvd.
16th Floor
Los Angeles, CA 90067
Pop music group

Thornburgh, Dick Lewis
Office of Governor
225 Main Capitol Bldg.
Harrisburg, PA 17120
Governor of Pennsylvania

Thorogood, George
P.O. Box 170
Kemblesville, PA 19347
Rock and roll guitarist, singer

Thrifty Corp.
3424 Wilshire Blvd.
Los Angeles, CA 90010
Leonard H. Straus,
chairman and CEO

Thurm, Joel
3000 W. Alameda Blvd.
Burbank, CA 91523
Casting director

Thurmond, Strom
Senate Office Bldg.
Washington, DC 20510
U. S. senator

Tiegs, Cheryl
c/o Eileen Ford
344 E. 59th St.
New York, NY 10022
Model

Tillis, Melvin
c/o Mel Tillis Enterprises
809 18th Ave. S.
Nashville, TN 37203-3218
Musician, songwriter

Time, Inc.
Time Life Bldg.
New York, NY 10020
J. Richard Munro,
president and CEO

Timex Group, Ltd.
Box 2126
Waterbury, CT 06722
T. F. Olsen, chairman

Tinker, Grant A.
c/o NBC-TV
3000 W. Alameda Blvd.
Burbank, CA 91523
Chairman of the board and CEO,
NBC

Tisch, Preston
Office of Postmaster General
Washington, DC 20066
U.S. postmaster general

Todd, Richard
598 Madison Ave.
New York, NY 10022
Football player

Todman, Howard Franklin
c/o Goodson-Todman
Productions
375 Park Ave.
New York, NY 10152
Television production company
exec.

Toland, John
One Long Ridge Rd.
Danbury, CT 06810
Pulitzer Prize–winning author

Toledano, Ralph De
825 New Hampshire Ave. NW.
Washington, DC 20037
Columnist, author, photographer

Tomlin, Lily
P.O. Box 27700
Los Angeles, CA 90027
Actress

Tonka Corp.
6000 Clearwater Dr.
Minnetonka, MN 55345
Stephen G. Shank,
chairman and CEO

Tony the Tiger
c/o Kellogg Co.
235 Porter
Battle Creek, MI 49017
Sugar Frosted Flakes Spokestiger

Tootsie Roll Industries, Inc.
7401 S. Cicero Ave.
Chicago, IL 60629
Melvin J. Gordon,
chairman and CEO

Torme, Mel (Melvin Howard Torme)
10100 Santa Monica Blvd.
16th Floor
Los Angeles, CA 90067
Musician, jazz vocalist

Torn, Rip (Elmore Torn, Jr.)
9200 Sunset Blvd., Suite 1210
Los Angeles, CA 90069
Actor, director

Toshiba of America, Inc.
375 Park Ave.
New York, NY 10152
N. Ishizaka,
chairman of the board, CEO

Toto
7250 Beverly Blvd., Suite 200
Los Angeles, CA 90036
Pop music group

Tourette Syndrome Association
42-40 Bell Blvd.
Bayside, NY 11361
Medical Self-Help Organization

Tower, John Goodwin
2201 C St., Room 7208
NW. Washington, DC 20520
Former senator, U.S. negotiator on strategic nuclear arms for U.S. del. to negotiations on nuclear and space arms

Townshend, Peter
c/o Entertainment Corp. of America
565 5th Ave.
New York, NY 10017
Rock guitarist, songwriter, singer

Toye, Clieve Roy
720 Spadina Ave., Suite 409
Toronto, ON., Canada
Professional soccer exec.

Toys "Я" Us, Inc.
395 W. Passaic St.
Rochelle Park, NJ 07662
Charles Lazarus,
chairman and CEO

Trail, George Arthur III
P.O. Box 2155
Johannesburg 2000
Republic of South Africa
*American consul general,
Johannesburg, South Africa*

Trailways, Inc.
1500 Jackson St.
Dallas, TX 75201
J. L. Kerigan, chairman and CEO

Trans World Airlines, Inc. (TWA)
605 3rd Ave.
New York, NY 10158
L. E. Smart, chairman

Trapp, Maria Augusta Von
Stowe, VT 05672
Musician, singer, author

Travanti, Daniel John
c/o Bauman Hiller & Associates
9220 Sunset Blvd.
Los Angeles, CA 90069
Actor

Travens, Colonel W. T., Jr.
P.O. Box 541
Hunt Valley, MD 21031
*President, Special Response
Corp., a company that controls
the use of drugs and alcohol in
the work place*

Travis, Randy
1610 16th Ave. S.
Nashville, TN 37212
Country music singer, songwriter

Travis, William W.
P.O. Box 26026
Birmingham, AL 35226
*Leading authority on the role of
sex in the Bible*

Travolta, John
1888 Century Park E., Suite 1400
Los Angeles, CA 90067
Actor

Treadway, Everett A.
5565 Sterret Pl., Suite 530
Columbia, MD 21044
*President, International Union of
Elevator Constructors*

Treesweet Products Co.
9801 Westeimer
Houston, TX 77042
C. E. Owens, chairman and CEO

Tree Top, Inc.
2nd and Railroad Aves.
Selah, WA 98942
Cragg Gilbert, chairman

Trevino, Lee Buck
14901 Quorum Dr., Suite 170
Dallas, TX 75240
Golfer

Trible, Paul Seward, Jr.
U.S. Senate Office Bldg.
Washington, DC 20510
U.S. senator

Trillo, Jesus Manuel (Manny)
P.O. Box 500
Station M
Montreal PQ HIV 3P2
Canada
Baseball player

Tripp, Paul
2 5th Ave.
New York, NY 10011
Actor, writer, lyricist

Triumph
3611 Mavis Rd., Uniot 3
Mississauga, ON. Canada
L5C 1T7
Rock band

Trudeau, Garry B.
c/o Universal Press Syndicate
4900 Main St.
Kansas City, MO 64112
*Cartoonist, creator of
"Doonesbury"*

Trudeau, Pierre Elliott
c/o Heenan Blaikie Jolin Potvin
Trepanier & Cobbett
1001 de Maisonneuve
Montreal PQ H3A 1M4 Canada
*Former prime minister of Canada,
lawyer*

Trumbull, Douglas
c/o Showscan Film Corp.
4503 Glencoe Ave.
Marina Del Rey, CA 90292
*Motion picture writer, director,
special effects artist*

Trump, Donald
c/o The Trump Organization
730 5th Ave.
New York, NY 10019
Real estate tycoon

TRW, Inc.
23555 Euclid Ave.
Cleveland, OH 44117
*Rubin F. Mettler,
chairman and CEO*

Tucker, Forrest
439 S. La Cienega Blvd., Suite 117
Los Angeles, CA 90048
Actor

Tucker, Tanya
2325 Crestmoor Rd.
Box 15245
Nashville, TN 37215
Singer

Tufarolo, James E.
P.O. Box 287
York, Pa 17405
Musician

Tuna, Charlie
c/o KHTZ Radio
3580 Wilshire Blvd.
Los Angeles, CA 90010
Radio personality

Tune, Tommy
c/o Marvin Shulman, Inc.
890 Broadway
New York, NY 10003
Musical theater director, actor

THE ADDRESS BOOK

Tureck, Rosalyn
c/o Columbia Artists
Management, Inc.
165 W. 57th St.
New York, NY 10019
*Concert artist, author, editor,
educator*

Turner, Kathleen
c/o The Gersh Agency Inc.
222 N. Canon Dr.
Beverly Hills, CA 90210
Actress

**Turner, Lana (Julia Jean
Mildred Frances Turner)**
9255 Sunset Blvd., Suite 1105
Los Angeles, CA 90069
Actress

**Turner, Ted
(Robert Edward Turner
III)**
P.O. Box 4064
Atlanta, GA 30302
*Broadcasting and sports exec.,
yachtsman*

**Turner, Tina
(Annie Mae Bullock
Turner)**
3575 Cahuenga Blvd. W.
Suite 580
Los Angeles, CA 90068
Entertainer

**Turner Broadcasting
System, Inc.**
100 International Blvd.
Atlanta, GA 30348-5366
*R. E. Turner, chairman and
president*

**Tutu, The Rt. Rev.
Desmond**
P.O. Box 1131
Johannesburg, South Africa
*Nobel Peace Prize winner,
bishop, anti-apartheid activist*

**Twentieth Century–Fox
Film Corp.**
10201 W. Pico Blvd.
Los Angeles, CA 90014
Barry Diller, chairman and CEO

Twitty, Conway
One Music Village Blvd.
Hendersonville, TN 37075
Country singer

Tyson, Cicely
1888 Century Park E., Suite 1400
Los Angeles, CA 90067
Actress

Tyson, Janet
c/o The Nashville Network
2806 Opryland Dr.
Nashville, TN 37214
Country western recording artist

Ueberroth, Peter Victor
Commissioner's Office
350 Park Ave.
New York, NY 10022
Commissioner of major league baseball

Uecker, Bob
c/o Milwaukee Brewers' Publicity Office
County Stadium
Milwaukee, WI 53214
Actor, radio announcer, former baseball player

Uggams, Leslie
151 El Camino Dr.
Beverly Hills, CA 90212
Entertainer

U-Haul International, Inc.
2727 N. Central Ave.
Phoenix, AZ 85004
William E. Carty, chairman

Ullmann, Liv
c/o Robert Lantz
114 E. 55th St.
New York, NY 10022
Actress

Union Carbide Corp.
Old Ridgebury Rd.
Danbury, CT 06810

*Warren M. Anderson,
chairman and CEO*

Union of Council for Soviet Jews
1411 K St. NW., Suite 402
Washington, DC 20005
Mark Epstein

Union Pacific Co.
345 Park Ave.
New York, NY 10154
*William S. Cook,
president, chairman, and CEO*

Unitas, John Constantine
c/o Johnny Unitas Golden Arm Restaurant
6354 York Rd.
Baltimore, MD 21212
Former football player, restaurateur

United Air Lines, Inc.
P.O. Box 66100
Chicago, IL 60666
*Richard J. Ferris,
chairman and CEO*

United Artists Corp.
10202 W. Washington Blvd.
Culver City, CA 90232
Richard Berger, president

United Cerebral Palsy Association
66 E. 34th St.
New York, NY 10016
James E. Introne, director

United Parcel Service of America, Inc.
Greenwich Office Park 5
Greenwich, CT 06831
John W. Rogers,
chairman and CEO

United Press International
220 E. 42nd St.
New York, NY 10017
Roderick W. Beaton,
president and CEO

United Van Lines, Inc.
One United Dr.
Fenton, Mo 63026
Maurice Greenblatt,
chairman of the board and CEO

Uniroyal, Inc.
World Headquarters
Middlebury, CT 06762
Joseph P. Flannery,
president, chairman, and CEO

U.S. Food and Drug Administration
5600 Fishers Lane (HFW-20)
Rockville, MD 20857
Bruce M. Brown

Unser, Al
7625 Central Ave. W.
Albuquerque, NM 87105
Race car driver

Updike, John Hoyer
c/o Alfred A. Knopf
201 E. 50th St.
New York, NY 10022
Writer

The Upjohn Co.
7000 Portage Rd.
Kalamazoo, MI 49001
R. T. Parfet, Jr.,
chairman and CEO

Upshaw, Eugene
c/o NFL Players Association
1300 Connecticut Ave.
NW. Washington, DC 20036
Executive director, NFL Players Association

Urich, Robert
409 N. Camden Dr., Suite 202
Beverly Hills, CA 90210
Actor

Uris, Leon
c/o Doubleday & Co.
245 Park Ave.
New York, NY 10167
Author

Ustinov, Peter
c/o William Morris Agency
UK Ltd.
147-149 Wardone St.
London W1 England
Actor, writer, director

Vaccaro, Brenda
151 El Camino Dr.
Beverly Hills, CA 90212
Actress

Valenti, Jack Joseph
1600 I St.
NW. Washington, DC 20006
Director, American Film Institute

Valentine, Karen
4141 Knobhill Dr.
Sherman Oaks, CA 91403
Actress

Valenzuela, Fernando
c/o Los Angeles Dodgers, Dodger
Stadium
1000 Elysian Park Ave.
Los Angeles, CA 90012
Baseball player

**Valli, Frankie
(Frank Castelluccio)**
151 El Camino Dr.
Beverly Hills, CA 90212
*Singer, formerly with
The Four Seasons*

Valvoline Oil Co.
P.O. Box 14000
Lexington, KY 40512
J. F. Boehm, president

Van Ark, Joan
151 El Camino Dr.
Beverly Hills, CA 90212
Actress

**Van Buren, Abigail
(Pauline Friedman
Phillips)**
9200 Sunset Blvd., Suite 1003
Los Angeles, CA 90069
*Columnist, writer, author,
lecturer, aka "Dear Abby"*

Vance, Cyrus Roberts
c/o Simpson Thacher & Bartlett
One Battery Park Plaza
New York, NY 10004
Lawyer, former secretary of state

Vancisin, Joseph Richard
P.O. Box 307
Branford, CT 06405
*Executive director, National
Association of Basketball Coaches*

Van Cleef, Lee
427 N. Canon Dr., Suite 205
Beverly Hills, CA 90210
Actor

Van De Kamp's Frozen Foods
6621 E. Pacific Coast Highway
Los Beach, CA 90803
Steven Pokress, president

Vanderbilt, Gloria Morgan
c/o Mujani U.S.A.
498 7th Ave.
New York, NY 10018
Fashion designer, artist, actress

Van Devere, Trish
c/o Harry Gold
12725 Ventura Blvd.
Studio City, CA 91604
Actress

Vandiver, Frank Everson
c/o Texas A&M University
College Station, TX 77840
President of Texas A&M University, author, educator

Van Dreelen, John
c/o Paul Kohner, Inc.
9169 Sunset Blvd.
Hollywood, CA 90069
Actor

Vandross, Luther
8271 Melrose Ave.
Los Angeles, CA 90046
Soul singer

Van Dyke, Dick
151 El Camino Dr.
Beverly Hills, CA 90212
Actor, comedian

Van Halen
10100 Santa Monica Blvd.
Suite 2340
Los Angeles, CA 90067
Rock band

Van Kamp, Merete
9123 Sunset Blvd.
Los Angeles, CA 90069
Actress

Vannelli, Gino
9034 Sunset Blvd., Suite 250
Los Angeles, CA 90069
Singer, Composer

Van Patten, Dick Vincent
132 Lasky Dr.
Beverly Hills, CA 90212
Actor

Van Patten, James
9200 Sunset Blvd., Suite 808
Los Angeles, CA 90069
Actor

Varley, John Herbert
2030 W. 28th St.
Eugene, OR 97405
Author

Vaughn, Robert (Francis Vaughn)
8899 Beverly Blvd.
Los Angeles, CA 90048
Actor

Vaughan, Sarah Lois
10100 Santa Monica Blvd.
16th Floor
Los Angeles, CA 90067
Singer

Vega, Suzanne
1500 Broadway, Suite 1703
New York, NY 10036
Singer, songwriter

Velasquez, Jorge Luis, Jr.
20 E. 46th St., Room 901
New York, NY 10017
Jockey

Vera, Billy
8730 Sunset Blvd., Penthouse W.
Los Angeles, CA 90069
Singer, songwriter, musician

Verdon, Gwen
c/o Shapiro Taxon and Kopell
11 W. 40th St.
New York, NY 10018
Dancer, actress, choreographer

Vereen, Ben
1350 Ave. of the Americas
New York, NY 10019
Actor, singer, dancer

Versace, Gianni
c/o Gianni Versace, Inc.
600 Madison Ave.
New York, NY 10022
Fashion designer

Vidal, Gore
c/o Random House
201 E. 50th St.
New York, NY 10022
Writer

Vigoda, Abe
c/o Contemporary Artists, Ltd.
132 Lasky Dr.
Beverly Hills, CA 90212
Actor

Villechaize, Herve Jean Pierre
P.O. Box 1305
Burbank, CA 91507
Actor

Vincent, Jan-Michael
P.O. Box 4475
North Hollywood, CA 91607
Actor

Vinton, Bobby (Stanley Robert Vinton)
P.O. Box 906
Malibu, CA 90265-0906
Entertainer

Vittadini, Adrienne
c/o Adrienne Vittadini Inc.
575 7th Ave.
New York, NY 10018
Fashion designer

Vlasic Foods, Inc.
33200 W. 14 Mile Rd.
W. Bloomingfield, MI 48033
Robert J. Vlasic, chairman

Voight, Jon
6464 Sunset Blvd., Suite 1150
Los Angeles, CA 90028
Actor

Volkswagen of America, Inc.
888 W. Big Beaver
Troy, MI 48007
Carl H. Hahn, chairman

Von Bulow, Claus
960 5th Ave.
New York, NY 10021
Acquitted of charges he murdered his wealthy wife

Von Furstenberg, Diane Simone Michelle
c/o Apparel Industries
1407 Broadway
New York, NY 10018
Fashion designer

Vonnegut, Kurt, Jr.
99 Park Ave., 25th Floor
New York, NY 10016
Writer

Vons Grocery Co.
10150 Lower Azusa Rd.
El Monte, CA 91731
William S. Davila, president

Von Sydow, Max Carl Adolf
c/o Paul Kohner Inc.
9169 Sunset Blvd.
Los Angeles, CA 90069
Actor

Wagner, Lindsay J.
1888 Century Park E., Suite 1400
Los Angeles, CA 90067
Actress

Wagner, Robert
151 El Camino Dr.
Beverly Hills, CA 90212
Actor

Wagoner, Porter
c/o World Class Talent
1522 Demonbreun St.
Nashville, TN 37203
Country music singer, composer

Waite, Ralph
1888 Century Park E., Suite 1400
Los Angeles, CA 90067
Actor

Waits, Thomas Alan
c/o Rothberg-Gerber
Management
145 Central Park W.
New York, NY 10023
Composer, singer, actor

Wakeman, Rick
c/o A&M Records
1416 N. La Brea Ave.
Hollywood, CA 90028
*Keyboardist, songwriter, enter-
tainer*

Walgreen Co.
200 Wilmot Rd.
Deerfield, IL 60015
*Charles R. Walgreen III,
chairman and CEO*

Walken, Christopher
8899 Beverly Blvd.
Los Angeles, CA 90048
Actor

Walker, Jimmy
9000 Sunset Blvd., Suite 400
Los Angeles, CA 90069
Actor

Walker, Marcy
c/o NBC
3000 W. Alameda Ave.
Burbank, CA 91523
Actress

Walker, Mort
c/o King Features Syndicate
235 E. 45th St.
New York, NY 10017
*Cartoonist, creator of "Beetle
Bailey"*

**Walker, Nancy
(Ann Myrtle Swoyer)**
9744 Wilshire Blvd., Suite 308
Beverly Hills, CA 90212
Actress

Walker, Sydney Smith, Jr.
450 Geary St.
San Francisco, CA 94102
Actor, educator

Walker, Wesley
598 Madison Ave.
New York, NY 10022
Football player

Wallace, Christopher
c/o NBC News
4001 Nebraska Ave.
NW. Washington, DC 20016
*NBC News White House
correspondent*

Wallace, Dee
9738 Arby Dr.
Beverly Hills, CA 90210
Actress

Wallace, George Corley
State Capitol
Montgomery, AL 36130
Governor of Alabama

Wallace, Irving
P.O. Box 49328
Los Angeles, CA 90049
Author

Wallace, Mike
c/o CBS News
524 W. 57th St.
New York, NY 10019
Cohost, CBS's 60 Minutes

Wallach, Eli
1888 Century Park E., Suite 1400
Los Angeles, CA 90067
Actor

Wallop, Malcolm
Russell Senate Office Bldg.
Room 206
Washington, DC 20510
U.S. senator

**Walsh, Joe
(Joseph Fidler Walsh)**
9044 Melrose Ave., 3rd Floor
Los Angeles, CA 90069
Rock guitarist, singer, songwriter

Walsh, Ulysses (Jim Walsh)
225 N. Maple St.
Vinton, VA 24179
Author

Walston, Ray
7550 Sunset Blvd.
Hollywood, CA 90046
Actor

Walter, Jessica
c/o Phil Gersh Agency
222 N. Canon Dr.
Beverly Hills, CA 90210
Actress

Walters, Barbara
c/o ABC News
1330 Ave. of the Americas
New York, NY 10019
Newscaster

**Walton, Bill
(William Theodore
Walton)**
c/o Boston Celtics
Boston Garden, North Station
Boston, MA 02114
Basketball player

Wanamaker, Sam
151 El Camino Dr.
Beverly Hills, CA 90212
Actor, director

Wang Chung
10100 Santa Monica Blvd.
16th Floor
Los Angeles, CA 90067
Pop music group

Wang Laboratories, Inc.
One Industrial Ave.
Lowell, MA 01851
*An Wang,
president, chairman, and CEO*

Ward, Charles
888 7th Ave.
New York, NY 10106
Actor, singer, dancer

Ward, Rachel
10100 Santa Monica Blvd.
16th Floor
Los Angeles, CA 90067
Actress

Warden, Jack
c/o Agency for Performing
Arts, Inc.
888 7th Ave.
New York, NY 10106
Actor

War on Drugs, Inc.
Route 3, Box 372
Sanford, FL 32771
Dr. Merle E. Parker

Warne, William Elmo
2090 8th Ave.
Sacramento, CA 95818
Irrigationist

Warner, John William
Russell Senate Office Bldg.
Room 421
Washington, DC 20510
U.S. senator

Warner, Malcolm Jamahl
c/o NBC
3000 W. Alameda Blvd.
Burbank, CA 91523
Actor

**Warner Communications,
Inc.**
75 Rockefeller Plaza
New York, NY 10019
*Stephen J. Ross,
chairman and CEO*

Warren, Michael
15760 Ventura Blvd., Suite 1730
Encino, CA 91436
Actor

Warrick, Ruth
c/o ABC Public Relations
1330 Ave. of the Americas
New York, NY 10019
Actress

Warwick, Dionne
9200 Sunset Blvd., Suite 420
Los Angeles, CA 90069
Singer

Washington Post Co.
1150 15th St. NW.
Washington, DC 20071
Katherine Graham,
chairman and CEO

Waters, Roger
c/o Premier Talent Agency
3 E. 54th St.
New York, NY 10022
Musician, singer, songwriter

Waterston, Samuel Atkinson
9000 Sunset Blvd., Suite 315
Los Angeles, CA 90069
Actor

Watkins, Curtis
1749 Pickney Rd.
Howell, MI 48843
World's only hypho-artist

Watson, Doc
c/o Manny Greenhill Management
1671 Appian Way
Santa Monica, CA 90401
Vocalist, guitarist, songwriter,
recording artist

Watson, Thomas Sturges
1313 Commerce Tower
Kansas City, MO 64105
Golfer

Watt, James Gaius
Box 3705
Jackson Hole, WY 83001
Lawyer, former secretary of the
interior

Waxman, Albert Samuel
c/o Pendergasts Talent Co. Ltd.
105 Dupont St.
Toronto, ON. M5R 1V4
Canada
Actor

WD-40 Co.
P. O. Box 80607
San Diego, CA 92138
John S. Barry, president

Weaver, Dennis
1930 Century Park W. Suite 303
Los Angeles, CA 90067
Actor

Weaver, Fritz William
c/o Lucy Kroll Agency
390 West End Ave.
New York, NY 10024
Actor

**Weaver, Sigourney
(Susan Weaver)**
8899 Beverly Blvd.
Los Angeles, CA 90048
Actress

Webber, Robert
10351 Santa Monica Blvd.
2nd Floor
Los Angeles, CA 90025
Actor

Webster Dictionary Corp.
3748 W. Montrose
Chicago, IL 60618-1027
*Paul Bieles, chairman and
president*

Wedgeworth, Ann
409 N. Camden Dr., Suite 202
Beverly Hills, CA 90210
Actress

Weeks, Wilford Frank
c/o Cold Regions Research
72 Lyme Rd.
Hanover, NH 03755
Glaciologist

**Weicker, Lowell Palmer,
Jr.**
Hart Senate Office Bldg.
Room 303
Washington, DC 20510
U.S. senator

**Weight Watchers
International**

800 Community Dr.
Manhasset, NY 11030
Albert Lippert, chairman

**Weinberger, Casper
Willard**
c/o Department of Defense
Room 3E880
The Pentagon
Washington, DC 20301
*U.S. secretary of defense for
Reagan administration*

Weiss, Donald Logan
410 Park Ave.
New York, NY 10022
*Executive director, National
Football League .*

Weitz, Bruce
10100 Santa Monica Blvd.
16th Floor
Los Angeles, CA 90067
Actor

Welch, Raquel
c/o Raquel Welch Productions
146 Central Park W.
New York, NY 10023
Actress

Welch Foods, Inc.
100 Main St.
Concord, MA 01742
J. Roy Orton, chairman

**Weld, Tuesday
(Susan Ker Weld)**
c/o Viderman Oberman &
Associates
103 W. Pico Blvd.
Los Angeles, CA 90015
Actress

Weller, Peter
c/o Bill Truesch Associates
853 7th Ave.
New York, NY 10019
Actor

Weller, William
5999 Butterfield Rd.
Hillside, IL 60162
*President, S&H Motivation.
Company sells motivation pro-
grams that help improve produc-
tivity of workers*

**Wells, Kitty
(Muriel Deason Wright)**
P.O. Box 809
Goodlettsville, TN 37072
Country singer

**Wendelstedt, Harry
Hunter, Jr.**
c/o Major League Umpires
Association
88 S. St.
Ormond Beach, FL 32074
Baseball umpire

**Wendy's International,
Inc.**

4288 W. Dublin Granville Rd.
Dublin, OH 43017
*R. David Thomas, senior chairman
and founder*

**West, Dottie
(Dorothy Marie Marsh)**
c/o Agency for Performing Arts
9000 Sunset Blvd.
Los Angeles, CA 90069
Country singer

West, Morris Langlo
c/o Maurice Greenbaum
375 Madison Ave.
New York, NY 10017
Novelist

Western Air Lines, Inc.
Box 92005 World Way Postal
Center
Los Angeles, CA 90009
Lawrence H. Lee, chairman

Western Union Corp.
One Lake St.
Upper Saddle River, NJ 07458
*Robert S. Leventhal,
chairman, president, and CEO*

**Westin, Av
(Avram Robert Westin)**
c/o ABC News
7 W. 66th St.
New York, NY 10023
Executive producer, ABC News

Westinghouse Electric Corp.
Gateway Center
Westinghouse Bldg.
Pittsburgh, PA 15222
D. D. Danforth,
chairman and CEO

Westmoreland, Gen. William
107&1/2 Tradd St.
Box 1059
Charleston, SC 29401
Commander of forces during Vietnam War

Weston, Jack
9200 Sunset Blvd., Suite 1009
Los Angeles, CA 90069
Actor

Whelchel, Lisa
P.O. Box 469
Mt. Pleasant, TX 75455
Actress

Whipple, Fred Lawrence
60 Garden St.
Cambridge, MA 02138
Astronomer

Whirlpool Corp.
Administrative Center
Benton Harbor, MI 49022
Jack D. Sparks,
chairman, president, and CEO

The Whispers
9229 Sunset Blvd., Suite 414
West Los Angeles, CA 90069
Pop music group

Whitaker, John Francis
c/o ABC Sports
1330 Ave. of the Americas
New York, NY 10019
Television sportscaster

White, Betty
151 El Camino Dr.
Beverly Hills, CA 90212
Actress

White, Byron
c/o U.S. Supreme Court Bldg.
One First St.
NE. Washington, DC 20543
Associate justice, U.S. Supreme Court

White, Frank, Jr.
P.O. Box 1969
Kansas City, MO 64141
Baseball player

White, Jesse Marc
c/o Lou Sherrell Agency
7060 Hollywood Blvd.
Hollywood, CA 90028
Actor

White, John Sylvester
9021 Melrose Ave., Suite 304
Los Angeles, CA 90069
Actor

White, Mark Wells, Jr.
Box 12428, Capitol Station
Austin, TX 78711
Governor of Texas

White, Vanna
9454 Wilshire Blvd., Penthouse
Beverly Hills, CA 90212
Letter-turner on Wheel of Fortune,
author

Whitesnake
c/o Frontline Management
80 Universal City Plaza
Universal City, CA 91608
Rock band

Whiting, E. Gale, Jr.
c/o Alta Bates
3001 Colby St.
Berkeley, CA 94705
Nuclear medicine specialist

Slim Whitman Appreciation Society of the U.S.
1002 W. Thurber St.
Tucson, AZ 85705
Loren R. Knapp, president

Whitmore, James
10000 Santa Monica Blvd.
Suite 305
Los Angeles, CA 90067
Actor

Whodini
298 Elizabeth St.
New York, NY 10012
Rap group

Widmark, Richard
8899 Beverly Blvd.
Los Angeles, CA 90048
Actor

Wiesel, Elie
c/o Boston University
745 Commonwealth Ave.
Boston, MA 02215
Religion educator, author, humanitarian

Wilcox, Larry
15301 Ventura Blvd., Suite 345
Sherman Oaks, CA 91403
Actor

Wilde, Cornel
c/o Jess Morgan U Co., Inc.
6420 Wilshire Blvd.
Los Angeles, CA 90048
Actor, producer, director

Wilde, Kim
c/o International Creative Management
40 W. 57th St.
New York, NY 10019
Pop singer

Wilder, Billy
P.O. Box 93877
Hollywood, CA 90093
Motion picture writer, producer, director

Wilder, Gene
9350 Wilshire Blvd., Suite 316
Beverly Hills, CA 90212
Actor, director, writer

Williams, Andy
c/o CBS Records
51 W. 52nd St.
New York, NY 10019
Entertainer

Williams, Billy Dee
8966 Sunset Blvd.
Hollywood, CA 90069
Actor

Williams, Don
c/o Jim Halsey Co., Inc.
3225 S. Norwood St.
Tulsa, OK 74135
Country singer, songwriter

Williams, Hank, Jr.
P.O. Box 850
Paris, TN 38242
Country music singer, songwriter, musician

Williams, Joe
On the Bandstand, Box C
River Edge, NJ 07661
Jazz and blues singer

Williams, John Towner
c/o Boston Pops Orchestra
301 Massachusetts Ave.
Boston, MA 02115
Composer, conductor

Williams, Paul
c/o 20th Century–Fox
Music Corp.
8544 N. Sunset Blvd.
Los Angeles, CA 90069
Singer, composer

Williams, Treat
c/o Jay Julien
1501 Broadway
New York, NY 10036
Actor

Williamson, Nicol
151 El Camino Dr.
Beverly Hills, CA 90212
Actor

Willis, Bruce
10100 Santa Monica Blvd.
16th Floor
Los Angeles, CA 90067
Actor, singer

Wilson, Flip
1350 Ave. of the Americas
New York, NY 10019
Comedian

Wilson, Nancy
5455 Wilshire Blvd., Suite 1002
Los Angeles, CA 90036
Singer

Wilson, Pete Barton
Hart Senate Office Bldg.
Room 720
Washington, DC 20510
U.S. senator

Wilson, Tom
P.O. Box 419149
Kansas City, MO 64141
Cartoonist, creator of "Ziggy"

Winchell's Donut House
16424 Valley View
La Mirada, CA 90638
Verne H. Winchell,
chairman of the board

Windom, William
6217 Glen Airey Dr.
Los Angeles, CA 90068
Actor

Winfield, Paul Edward
10000 Santa Monica Blvd.
Suite 305
Los Angeles, CA 90067
Actor

Winfrey, Oprah
P.O. Box 909715
Chicago, IL 60690
Television talk show host

Winkler, Henry Franklin
151 El Camino Dr.
Beverly Hills, CA 90212
Actor

Winnebago Industries, Inc.
Junction 9 and 69
Forest City, IA 50436
Ronald E. Haugen,
president and CEO

Winslow, Kellen
P.O. Box 20666
San Diego, CA 92120
Football player

Winter, Johnny
(John Dawson Winter III)
c/o Premier Talent Agency
3 E. 54th St.
New York, NY 10022
Guitarist, songwriter

Winters, Jonathan
c/o George Spota
11151 Ophir Dr.
Los Angeles, CA 90024
Actor, comedian, author

Winters, Shelley
8899 Beverly Blvd.
Los Angeles, CA 90048
Actress

Winwood, Stephen Lawrence
9200 Sunset Blvd., Penthouse 15
Los Angeles, CA 90069
Musician, singer, composer

Wiswall, Frank Lawrence, Jr.
11870-D Sunrise Valley Dr.
Reston, VA 22091-3303
Admiralty lawyer

Woititz, Janet
Institute for Counseling
118 Pompton Ave.
Verona, NJ 07044
Author, Adult Children of
Alcoholics

**Wolfe, Tom
(Thomas Kennerly Wolfe, Jr.)**
c/o Farrar Straus & Giroux, Inc.
19 Union Square W.
New York, NY 10003
Author, journalist

**Wonder, Stevie
(Stevland Morris)**
c/o Chrysanthemum James Black
Bull Music
4616 Magnolia Blvd.
Burbank, CA 91505
Singer, musician, composer

Woods, James
1888 Century Park E., Suite 1400
Los Angeles, CA 90067
Actor

**Woodward, Joanne
Gignilliat**
59 Coleytown Rd.
Westport, CT 06880
Actress

F. W. Woolworth Co.
233 Broadway
New York, NY 10279
John W. Lynn, chairman and CEO

World Boxing Federation
P.O. Box 4520
Greenwich, CT 06830
Vince McMahon, president

Wouk, Herman
c/o BSW Literary Agency
3255 N St. NW.
Washington, DC 20007
Author

Wyman, Jane
c/o Lorimar Productions
3970 Overland Ave.
Culver City, CA 90230
Actress, exwife of Ronald Reagan

Wynter, Dana
c/o Contemporary Artists, Ltd.
132 Lasky Dr.
Beverly Hills, CA 90212
Actress

Mr. X
c/o "The Greenhouse"
1185 W. 30th St.
Los Angeles, CA 90067
*"The Most Inconspicuous Man in
the World"*

Xerox Corp.
Stamford, CT 06904
David T. Kearns,
chairman and CEO

Yablans, Frank
c/o Frank Yablans Presentations, Inc.
10202 W. Washington Blvd.
Culver City, CA 90230
Motion picture producer

Yarborough, William
c/o National Association of Stock Car Auto Racing
1801 Volusia Ave.
Daytona Beach, FL 32015
Stock car racer

Yarrow, Peter
8899 Beverly Blvd.
Los Angeles, CA 90048
Folk singer with Peter, Paul, and Mary

Yeager, Charles Elwood
P.O. Box 128
Cedar Ridge, CA 95924
First man to fly faster than speed of sound

Yellow Cab Co.
2501 W. Lexington St.
Baltimore, MD 21203
George J. Joseph, president

Yoakam, Dwight
17351 Sunset Blvd.

Pacific Palisades, CA 90272
Country music singer, songwriter

York, Michael
(Michael York-Johnson)
9000 Sunset Blvd., Suite 1200
Los Angeles, CA 90069
Actor

York, Susannah
8899 Beverly Blvd.
Los Angeles, CA 90048
Actress

Yothers, Tina
c/o NBC
3000 W. Alameda Ave.
Burbank, CA 91523
Actress

Young, Burt
10100 Santa Monica Blvd.
16th Floor
Los Angeles, CA 90067
Actor

Young, Chyrl
6537 Raeford Rd., Number 104
Fayetteville, NC 28304
President, Stork News. Company rents 8-foot stork with bundle hanging from mouth to announce new arrivals

THE ADDRESS BOOK

Young, Coleman Alexander
Office of Mayor
2 Woodward Ave.
Detroit, MI 48226
Mayor of Detroit

Young, Neil
c/o Lookout Management
8919 Sunset Blvd.
Los Angeles, CA 90069
Musician, songwriter

Young, Robert
1901 Ave. of the Stars, Suite 840
Los Angeles, CA 90067
Actor

Youngman, Henny
10 Munson Ct.
Melville, NY 90704
Comedian

Young & Rubicam, Inc.
285 Madison Ave.
New York, NY 10017
*Edward N. Ney,
chairman and CEO*

Youth for Understanding International Exchange
3501 Newark St. NW.
Washington, DC 20016-3167
*Cameron C. Dubes,
director of public affairs.*

Yugo America, Inc.
28 Park Way
Upper Saddle River, NJ 07458
*Malcolm N. Bricklin,
chairman of the board*

Zadora, Pia
Trump Tower
725 5th Ave.
New York, NY 10022
Actress

Zale Corp.
901 W. Walnut Hill Lane
Irving, TX 75038
Donald Zale, chairman

Zanuck, Richard
202 N. Canon Dr.
Beverly Hills, CA 90210
Motion picture executive

Zapata, Carmen
328 S. Beverly Dr., Suite E
Beverly Hills, CA 90212
Actress

Zawinul, Joe
c/o CBS Records
51 W. 52nd St.
New York, NY 10019
*Bandleader, composer,
keyboardist*

Zeffirelli, Franco
Via Due Macelli 31
Rome, Italy
*Motion picture and theater
director*

Zenith Electronics Corp.
1000 N. Milwaukee Ave.
Glenview, IL 60025
*Jerry K. Pearlman,
chairman, president, and CEO*

Zerbe, Anthony
c/o Smith Freedman & Associates
9869 Santa Monica Blvd.
Beverly Hills, CA 90212
Actor

Zevon, Warren
1350 Ave. of the Americas
New York, NY 10019
Singer, songwriter

Zimbalist, Stephanie
4024 Radford Ave.
Studio City, CA 91604
Actress

Zorinsky, Edward
Russell Senate Office Bldg.
Room SR443
Washington, DC 20510
U.S. senator

ZZ Top
P.O. Box 19647
Houston, TX 77224
Rock and roll band